impact
WORKBOOK 4

SERIES EDITORS
JoAnn (Jodi) Crandall
Joan Kang Shin

Unit 1	Pushing the Limits	2
Unit 2	It Takes a Village	12
	Units 1–2 Review	**22**
Unit 3	Food Matters	24
Unit 4	The Footprint of Fun	34
	Units 3–4 Review	**44**
Unit 5	Why We Explore	46
Unit 6	Giants	56
	Units 5–6 Review	**66**
Unit 7	Creative Problem-Solving	68
Unit 8	Art Connections	78
	Units 7–8 Review	**88**
	Choice Activities	**90**

Australia • Brazil • Mexico • Singapore • United Kingdom • United States

Unit 1
Pushing the Limits

1 **Match the word to its definition or description.** Write the letter on the line.

_____ 1. mental

_____ 2. obstacles

_____ 3. achieved

_____ 4. hazardous

_____ 5. boundary

_____ 6. physical

_____ 7. opponent

_____ 8. unreachable

a. Someone who plays against you.

b. He learned skydiving. He realized his dream.

c. It's something that separates two places.

d. It's too high. I can't touch it.

e. A difficult puzzle provides this type of challenge.

f. The desert conditions were dangerous.

g. He faces many difficulties.

h. Mountain climbing requires this type of strength.

2 **Fill in the blank with the correct word from Activity 1.**

1. She _____ her goal and won the gold medal.

2. There were many _____ to overcome.

3. The weather conditions were extreme and _____ .

4. This difficult math problem requires great _____ effort.

5. The top of the mountain was _____ .

6. He beat his _____ .

7. These trees mark the _____ between the two houses.

8. Rock climbing takes unbelievable _____ effort.

3. **Look at the pictures.** Then listen to each situation. Choose the correct word from the box and write it under the picture that describes it. **TR: 2**

| endurance | pain | role model | determination | push himself | extreme |

_____

_____

_____

_____

_____

_____

4. **Write.** Use each word from Activity 3 in a sentence.

1. _____
2. _____
3. _____
4. _____
5. _____
6. _____

GRAMMAR

Embedded statements, questions, and commands

I think... Avalanches are very dangerous.	<u>I think</u> **avalanches are** very dangerous.
I wonder... How difficult is that climb?	<u>I wonder</u> **how difficult that climb is.**
Do you know... Is it safe to climb that mountain in the fall?	<u>Do you know</u> **if it's safe to climb that mountain in the fall**?
I'm telling you... Be careful on the ice!	<u>I'm telling you</u> **to be careful on the ice**!

You can make statements, ask questions, or give commands indirectly using verbs like *think*, *wonder*, or *tell*. When you ask an indirect question, pay attention to word order. If the answer to a question is *yes* or *no*, you need to use *if*. When you give an indirect command, you need to use *to* followed by an infinitive.

5 **Read the sentences.** Rewrite them using embedded statements, questions, and commands.

1. Nontraditional sports are becoming popular.

   I think _nontraditional sports are becoming popular_ .

2. Buy the right equipment for surfing.

   I'm telling you _____.

3. How many ski races do you go to every year?

   I'd like to know _____.

4. How do we get to the top of the mountain from here?

   We're not sure _____.

5. Why do people push themselves to their limits?

   I wonder _____.

6. Put away the mountain bike.

   My mom is asking me _____.

6 **Unscramble the words.** Write embedded statements, questions, and commands. Pay attention to word order.

1. role / good / models / think / set / I / examples

   I think role models set good examples.

2. extreme / I / endurance / guess / sports / unbelievable / require

   _____

3. when / next / the / wonder / marathon / I / is

   _____

4. sporting events / go to / what / you / asking / I'm / you

   _____

5. slow / I'm / down / you / asking / to

   _____

6. snowboarding / he / a lot of / thinks / training / requires

   _____

7. train / you/ during / if / the / like / months / winter / I'd / to know

   _____

7 **Listen.** Write the questions as embedded statements. **TR: 3**

1. I wonder *who your role model is* _____ .

2. Can you tell me _____ ?

3. I'd like to know _____ .

4. I'd also like to know _____ .

5. I'm curious to find out _____ .

6. I'd like to know _____ .

5

8 **Listen and read.** As you read, notice what makes Laura a good role model. **TR: 4**

A DETERMINED YOUNG WOMAN

When Laura Dekker was 13, she had a dream. Her dream was to sail around the world on her own. Her passion for sailing started when she was young. She was born on a boat and spent the first five years of her life at sea. By the time she was seven, she was sailing in competitive races. Over the years, she learned everything about sailing and weather systems. When she was ten, she bought her own sailboat with money she saved. It seemed that there was no stopping her.

However, it wasn't easy to follow her dream. The main obstacle she faced was not hazardous weather but her age. People told her she was too young. They said that sailing on her own was beyond her ability and that the journey could have serious consequences. With determination, however, Laura convinced everyone that she was capable of sailing around the world alone. She believed that her mental and physical skills enabled her to endure such a long journey.

Laura eventually set sail when she was 14. She sailed over 43,000 km (27,000 miles) and across 3 oceans. Her trip lasted 366 days. Life on the boat was a bit of a struggle, but she pushed herself. She had no refrigerator or washing machine. There was no shower, and she had to repair everything herself. She spent weeks on her own but used her time well. She kept a diary and completed classwork to help her finish high school.

Laura's determination helped her achieve her dream. After her trip, she spent time speaking about her experiences to adults and young people. She also wrote a book about her travels. She hasn't stopped sailing and says, "I still have a lot of dreams. You can never have enough of them."

9 **Read.** Circle the correct answers.

1. Laura wanted to sail because _____ .

   a. she bought a boat   b. it was her dream

2. Laura spent the first years of her life _____ .

   a. on a boat   b. on land

3. The main obstacle Laura faced was that she _____ to sail around the world on her own.

   a. wasn't the right age   b. had the right skills

4. It was Laura's _____ that helped her achieve her dream.

   a. studies   b. determination

5. While she sailed around the world, she _____ .

   a. repaired the washing machine   b. wrote and studied

6. Laura _____ .

   a. still sails and has dreams   b. spends all her time inspiring others

10 **Read the article again.** Fill in the timeline with Laura's age and the important event that happened at that point in her life.

LAURA'S TIMELINE

AGE   0   present

EVENT   Laura was born in 1995

11 **Write.** What do you need to do to accomplish your dream?

My dream is to _____

_____

To achieve my dream I need to _____

_____

GRAMMAR

Adding emphasis

My brother prefers living in the country to living in the city.	**The place (where)** my brother prefers to live **is** in the country.
I really admire Cory Richards' determination.	**The thing (that)** I really admire about Cory Richards **is** his determination.
The hikers hated camping out in hazardous weather.	**The reason (why)** the hikers hated camping **was** the hazardous weather.
I like kitesurfing. It pushes me to my physical and mental limits.	**What I like best about** kitesurfing **is that** it pushes me to my physical and mental limits.

We draw our listeners' attention to what is important by focusing on it. We say *where, when, who, why,* or *what* at the beginning of the sentence.

12 Listen. Then complete the dialogues. **TR: 5**

A: I love trying out new sports.

B: _____ is skydiving.

A: Skateboarding is great. You can do it anywhere.

B: _____ is that you don't need a lot of expensive equipment.

A: I'm planning to go scuba diving in the Red Sea next year.

B: _____ is the Great Barrier Reef!

13 Read. Then write a sentence emphasizing your preferences and reasons.

1. I love summer vacations.

   The thing (that) I love about summer vacations is that we go to the beach every day.

2. I like to travel and explore other countries.

   _____

3. I really want to meet a famous photographer.

   _____

4. I prefer team sports.

   _____

14 **Read the advertisement.** Answer the questions. Give your reason and be sure to add emphasis in your answers.

Are you adventurous? Do you want to try a sport that will push you to your physical limits and help you connect with nature?

Extreme-Dream Sports offers a range of extreme sports in locations all over the world. We have experienced teachers who know how to make their sport easy to learn. Our vacation trips include transportation and hotel. We also provide all the equipment you need to make your new adventure a success.

This year we have two new extreme sports for you to try!

First, we offer kitesurfing. It takes place on a beautiful tropical island. It's the perfect location to try this new sport—with its light winds and gentle waves. Palm trees surround our golden beaches. After a hard day of training, you can relax on the beach with a cool coconut drink.

Our sandboarding classes are popular with the whole family. We have camps and offer group or individual classes. You will be in total control as you learn to slide down the rolling sand dunes. You will love the unbelievable sense of space and the freedom of being in a desert.

Why not try a new extreme sport? Check out our website for more information. Hope to see you soon!

1. Which extreme sport would you love to try?

   What I would love to try is sandboarding because I have never been in a desert.

2. Why would you want to try one of these extreme sports?

   _____

3. What would you love about sandboarding or kitesurfing?

   _____

4. Where would you really want to go on your next vacation?

   _____

9

WRITING

A biography tells the story of a person's life. We use words and expressions to help us connect ideas and describe the main events chronologically, in the order they happened.

- afterwards
- at first
- eventually
- later on

- little by little
- more recently
- today
- ultimately

15 Organize

1. Your topic is the *Biography of an athlete.* Do some research on the Internet about different athletes. Choose an athlete who inspires you and who you feel is a good role model for others. Use the writing box below to write the main events of the athlete's life in the correct order. Add dates. Choose events that show how your athlete became the role model he/she is today.

Name of athlete: _____
Born:
Event 1:
Event 2:
Event 3:

2. Plan your writing. You'll need an introductory paragraph with a topic sentence. Your topic sentence should state that you are going to write a biography about an athlete who is a role model for others. Explain why you have chosen this particular athlete. Write your explanation here:

_____

Write three paragraphs. Use the expressions above and your notes from the table to guide you. Describe your athlete's achievements using the words *at first* in your first paragraph, *afterwards,* in your middle paragraph, and *eventually/little by little* and *more recently/ today* in your third paragraph.

Finish your biography with a brief statement of why this athlete is a good role model.

16 Write

1. Go to p. 21 in your book. Reread the model and writing prompt.

2. Write your first draft. Check for organization, content, punctuation, capitalization, and spelling.

3. Write your final draft. Share it with your teacher and classmates.

Now I Can . . .

talk about extreme sports and overcoming obstacles.

☐ Yes, I can!
☐ I think I can.
☐ I need more practice.

Why do you think Cory and Amy are featured in this unit?

_____

What extreme sport or mental challenge would you like to try? Why?

_____

use embedded statements, questions, and commands.

☐ Yes, I can!
☐ I think I can.
☐ I need more practice.

Make sentences to form embedded statements, questions, and commands.

I think . . .	How will I beat my opponent?
I'm asking you to . . .	Some extreme sports are too dangerous.
I wonder . . .	Push yourself and do your best.

_____

_____

_____

use different word order for emphasis.

☐ Yes, I can!
☐ I think I can.
☐ I need more practice.

I always wanted a house on the beach.

The place (where) _____ .

I would like to try sandboarding.

The extreme sport (that) I would like to try _____ .

I love where I live because I can do a lot of sports.

The reason (why) _____ .

write a biography of an athlete who is also a role model.

☐ Yes, I can!
☐ I think I can.
☐ I need more practice.

Write about an athlete. Use the words in the box.

| at first | later on | more recently | was born in |

Choose an activity. Go to page 90.

Unit 2
It Takes a Village

1 **Read.** Complete the sentences. Then do the puzzle.

1. Photos taken from the air help us understand the _____ of the disaster.

2. When you _____ something, you look for the size or quantity of it.

3. The cost of something is its _____ .

4. A social _____ connects information between people and electronic devices.

5. Facts and information are examples of _____ .

6. In times of a _____ , people often help each other.

7. Researchers _____ , or watch, something for a special purpose over a period of time.

8. An _____ is the most recent information, such as news.

9. Computers _____ information or data very quickly.

10. Facts and signs provide _____ to show that something is true.

11. A _____ works to make other people's lives better.

12. To make something _____ means to make it greater in size.

13. Crisis mappers analyze information and _____ solutions.

What's the secret word? _____ Write a definition using your own words.

_____

_____

2 **Read.** Circle the correct word.

1. After the typhoon, rescuers **uploaded** / **expanded** a lot of pictures on social media.

2. Rescuers use modern technology to **monitor** / **expand** conditions after a hurricane.

3. Small earthquakes and volcanic ash provided **data** / **evidence** that the volcano was about to erupt.

4. Scientists collected and analyzed **crowdsourcing** / **data** for their research.

5. What if we went online and became digital **humanitarians** / **data** to help people in need?

6. Many organizations often use **crisis** / **crowdsourcing** to highlight environmental disasters and raise money.

3 **Fill in the blank with the correct word from Activity 1.**

1. Crisis mapping is _____*evidence*_____ that anyone can help those in need.

2. After an earthquake, a large _____ of water and food must be sent to the scene.

3. Computers can _____ information more quickly than humans.

4. Rescuers can use technology to _____ conditions after a disaster.

5. Scientists analyze _____ and study it for its meaning.

6. _____ work to help other people.

7. The news report gave the latest _____ about the destruction.

8. Avalanches can cause a major _____ .

9. The Internet allows people to _____ their communication.

10. It's difficult to _____ the level of the destruction after an earthquake.

11. A computer _____ helps people to share information.

12. Crisis maps help us see the _____ of a disaster.

13. The results of her research always _____ a lot of excitement.

13

GRAMMAR

Future tenses: Describing events in the future

Next summer, **I will coordinate** work at our local charity.
In the next few years, more people **will be collaborating** through crowdsourcing.
What **will you be doing** this time tomorrow?
By the end of next week, digital humanitarians **will have used** more data.

We use **will + infinitive** to talk about future events and situations. We also use it for predicting: *I think it will rain later.*

We use **will + be + -ing** to indicate an activity that is in progress at some point in the future.

We use **will + have + past participle** to indicate that an action will already be completed by a certain time in the future.

4 **Listen and complete the chart.** Then answer the questions in full sentences. **TR: 6**

Every day	_____ go online _____ and	_____ check _____	emails
Monday	_____ at photos		
Tuesday	_____ and	_____ photos	
Wednesday	_____ and	_____ text messages	
Thursday	_____ text messages		

1. Where will the students be volunteering?

   _____

2. What will they use to identify buildings with serious damage?

   _____

3. Who will they be sending text messages to on Wednesday?

   _____

4. What are the three tasks that the students will have done by Friday?

   _____

14

5 **Fill in the blank.** Complete each sentence with a word or words from the box.

good cause	fundraiser	help out	network	volunteers

A

1. She wants to _____ by cooking at the local community center.

2. The Spring Fair, with all its activities, will be an excellent _____ .

3. We will be taking part in a bike ride across the country to raise awareness for a _____ .

4. Marzan has a _____ of friends who live all over the world.

5. Organizers are hoping that more _____ will become digital humanitarians.

Match a sentence from A with a sentence in B. Write the number on the line. Underline examples of the future.

B

_____ a. By the end of the year, he will have visited them all!

_____ b. That way, they will be able to analyze data faster.

_____ c. By the end of the journey, we will have traveled through every major city.

_____ d. Next year she will give free cooking classes.

_____ e. Last year it raised over $5,000 for cancer research. This year we hope it will raise even more money.

6 **Answer the questions about your day tomorrow.**

1. Where will you be at midday tomorrow?

_____

2. What will you be doing in the afternoon?

_____

3. What will you have done by this time tomorrow?

_____

7 Listen and read. As you read, think about how the title and the saying are connected. **TR: 7**

The New Digital Global Community

There's an old saying: "It takes a village to bring up a child." This saying, or proverb, suggests that the community is just as important as the family when looking after a child. Both the family and the community share in the responsibility. Patrick Meier believes that new technologies do the same thing. He believes that digital technology is creating a global village where people care about and help each other in times of need.

One type of digital technology that has made it easy to be involved in local or global events is crowdsourcing. Now anyone can take action. All around the globe, people are networking for the greater good, and not only in times of crisis.

For example, digital volunteers have classified 4 million images of the surface of Mars. Without volunteers, this would have taken scientists many years to do.

In Russia, a cell phone alert tells blood donors that someone in their local area, with the same blood type, needs a blood donation. In India, people are using "unsmart" phones as a tool to report government actions.

In the United Kingdom, a site encourages older people who live alone to network and cook meals for each other. In the United States, a site for patients and families means they can share experiences of looking after very sick family members. It also provides a rich resource for medical researchers.

Nowadays, even animals benefit from digital technology! Across Africa and Asia, a website allows people to report on wildlife crimes.

The new digital global community is working together to research, explore, share, and survive disasters. It's becoming a worldwide village with digital humanitarians ready to be responsible for making the world a better place to live in.

16

8 Read. Circle the best answer.

1. The reading describes how _____ .
   a. a young engineer helped his community
   b. technology is bringing the world together

2. The reading gives _____ .
   a. a description of village life in Africa
   b. examples of the world finding solutions to its problems

3. In the reading, the author suggests that _____ .
   a. people are taking action locally and globally
   b. people only work together in times of natural disasters

4. The reading informs us that _____ .
   a. the Internet and cell phones are tools to help us face new challenges
   b. only people with the latest technology can be digital humanitarians

5. In the reading, we're given examples of how _____ .
   a. to use computer and smartphone apps effectively
   b. networking and crowdsourcing can benefit scientific research, medicine, and the environment

9 Look at the map. Add information that describes how each region uses crowdsourcing. Then research a different country or region that uses crowdsourcing. Add it to the map.

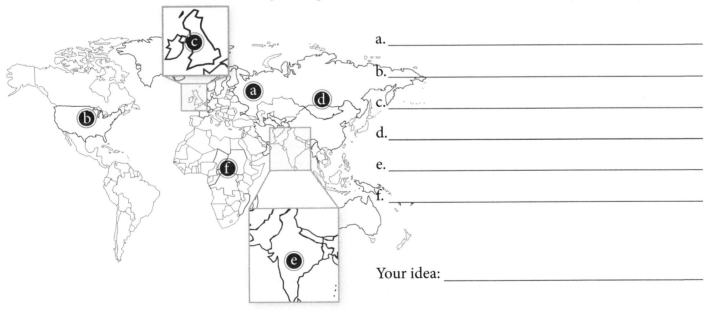

a. _____
b. _____
c. _____
d. _____
e. _____
f. _____

Your idea: _____

10 Write. In your notebook, explain your understanding of the proverb, "It takes a village to bring up a child." How have people outside your family influenced you?

17

GRAMMAR

Quantifiers: Expressing amounts

Half of / Fifty percent of the population **is** an online user.	**A lot of / Two-thirds of / Sixty-seven percent of** students **are** online users.
The majority of / Most of the community members **are** collaborating.	**The majority of / Most of** the community **is** collaborating.
A number of digital humanitarians **are** creating crisis maps.	**The number of** digital humanitarians **is** growing.

When you use expressions to talk about quantities, pay attention to the noun to decide if the verb is singular or plural. Remember that non-count nouns take a singular verb.

The expressions *a number of* and *the number of* are used with plural nouns. *A number of* means *some* and takes a plural verb. *The number of* refers to a specific quantity and takes a singular verb.

11 **Read.** Underline the quantifiers. Then listen and check *T* for *True* or *F* for *False*. Rewrite any false sentences as true. **TR: 8**

	T	**F**
1. Half of the people on the planet have a cell phone.	☐	☐
2. The number of text messages is increasing all the time.	☐	☐
3. One-third of all text messages contain a photo.	☐	☐
4. Less than 20 percent of people who text are under 18.	☐	☐
5. A large number of people over the age of 65 send messages.	☐	☐

_____

_____

_____

12 **Listen.** Circle the expression that summarizes the information about the event. **TR: 9**

1. **A lot of / A number of** people took part in the fundraising run.

2. **Over half of / A small number of** the students didn't show up.

3. **Two-thirds of / The majority of** the runners were students.

4. **A third of / More than 50 percent of** the runners finished the race in under an hour and 30 minutes.

13 **Read.** Then complete each sentence with a phrase from the box that can mean the same as the underlined words in the letter.

Dear Students,

We are organizing a Spring Fair at the school next month. We are very excited. We hope that by the end of the event, we'll have raised <u>thousands of dollars</u>. This will help build a new home for the elderly in our community.

As you know from last year, hundreds of parents attend our event. <u>At least 50 percent</u> of those parents will come with young children. We need <u>five</u> volunteers to do activities such as face painting and traditional games with the younger children.

We also need student volunteers to work at the stands. We will have 18 stands in total. <u>Six</u> of the stands will sell food. <u>The rest</u> of the stands will offer toys, crafts, and books.

We really look forward to your participation and hope that you can help out some of the time at the Spring Fair for this important cause.

Sincerely,

Mrs. Torres

School Principal

| the majority of | a small number of | half of | a lot of | a third of |

1. The school wants to raise _____ money for a good cause.

2. _____ the parents will come with young children.

3. The principal wants _____ students to do activities with young children.

4. _____ the stands will sell food.

5. _____ stands will sell toys, crafts, and books.

WRITING

In persuasive writing you need to convince your reader to share your opinion. It's important to state exactly why the reader should share your ideas and to support your statements with facts. The following expressions can help you:

- according to
- equally important / necessary
- it's clear that
- based on
- especially

14 Organize

1. Your topic is to *persuade your readers to take part in a local or global community service project.* Brainstorm projects that you are passionate about and choose one to write about. Write the name of your project on the line below. In the first column, list one or two reasons why people should join you in this campaign. In the second column, add important facts to support your reasons.

Name of your project _____

Reasons	Important Facts

2. Plan your writing. You'll need a general opening statement that describes the project and what needs to be done. For example: *There are nearly 2,500 items of garbage for every kilometer on a beach! We need people to ...*

Write your topic sentence here.

_____

3. You'll need two or three short paragraphs describing what work needs to be done and why it's important. Remember to provide evidence and/or facts in each paragraph to persuade your readers to join your project.

4. Finally, you'll need a concluding paragraph. It will summarize your campaign and include a "call to action" on the part of your readers.

15 Write

1. Go to p. 37 in your book. Reread the model and writing prompt.

2. Write your first draft. Check for organization, content, punctuation, capitalization, and spelling.

3. Check your final draft. Share it with your teacher and classmates.

Now I Can . . .

talk about digital humanitarians and crowdsourcing.

☐ Yes, I can!
☐ I think I can.
☐ I need more practice.

How has technology helped to bring communities together?

_____

How would you define a "crisis map" to a friend?

_____

use future tenses to describe events in the future.

☐ Yes, I can!
☐ I think I can.
☐ I need more practice.

| 2020 | 2021 | 2022 | 2023 | 2024 | 2025 |

September 2020
start college

2022–2023
work experience abroad

June 2024
finish college

I _____ college in September 2020.

Between 2022 and 2023, I _____ working abroad.

By June 2024, I _____ college.

use different expressions of quantity.

☐ Yes, I can!
☐ I think I can.
☐ I need more practice.

Choose the item that correctly completes each sentence.

1. The school raised _____ money at the fundraiser.

a. a number of   b. a lot of

2. _____ the community participates in crowdsourcing.

a. The number of   b. Half of

write a persuasive essay to convince someone to take part in a community service project.

☐ Yes, I can!
☐ I think I can.
☐ I need more practice.

Persuade your friends to participate in cleaning up a nearby park. Write three sentences using the phrases below.

| based on . . . | equally important . . . | it's clear . . . |

_____

_____

_____

Choose an activity. Go to page 91.

Units 1–2 Review

1 **Read the text.** Choose the best answer for each blank. The first one is done for you.

Vertical Ice Boundaries

You don't have to go out into (1) __b__ weather conditions to test your levels of (2) ____ . This (3) ____ sport will really make you push yourself to your physical (4) ____ .

It doesn't matter if you are an experienced climber or not, our indoor ice walls will give you an (5) ____ experience.

We have one-hour sessions every afternoon, but we also offer special training (6) ____ once a month. Our qualified teachers help new climbers (7) ____ their fear of heights and fear of falling. They also show techniques for using the equipment. With our teachers and your (8) ____ , you will reach your (9) ____ on our ice walls!

1. a. today's   b. hazardous   c. summer
2. a. struggle   b. pain   c. endurance
3. a. peak   b. nontraditional   c. boundary
4. a. limit   b. height   c. in control
5. a. expensive   b. unbelievable   c. outgoing
6. a. events   b. parties   c. sports
7. a. observe   b. overcome   c. achieve
8. a. determination   b. money   c. friends
9. a. role model   b. opponent   c. peak performance

2 **Read the text.** Choose the best word to fill each blank.

collaborate	crisis	crowdsourced	data	empowering	generate
monitor	network	process	scale	uploaded	

The Zooniverse is the world's largest online collection of people-powered science projects. Hundreds of thousands of people around the world (1) _____ with professional researchers. These digital volunteers help manage large amounts of (2) _____ which would be too much for researchers to (3) _____ alone. In one project, volunteers watched videos from 50 cameras focused on nesting penguins. They had to (4) _____ and record the birth of each chick.

Zooniverse has collaborated in many times of (5) _____ such as an earthquake. In Nepal, in 2015, they (6) _____ the mapping of the disaster area by analyzing thousands of images (7) _____ from people's cell phones. The images helped relief organizations understand the (8) _____ of the disaster and where help was needed.

Teachers use Zooniverse projects to (9) _____ students' interest. Everyone can play a part in this (10) _____ of digital humanitarians. It can be a very (11) _____ experience.

3 **Complete the second sentence so that it has a meaning similar to the first sentence.**

1. What would life be like on Mars?

   I wonder _____ .

2. Please put on a helmet when you go skiing.

   She's asking us _____ .

3. Can you upload the photos when you have looked at them?

   He is telling them to _____ .

4. I don't like extreme sports. You always need a lot of equipment.

   What I don't like _____ .

5. I really want to be a digital humanitarian so I can help others.

   The reason I _____ .

4 **Read the blog entry.** Check (✓) the correct statements.

Saturday, May 19

Tomorrow I will be revisiting my childhood. I will be looking through clothes and toys from when I was a child. By this time next week, we'll have moved to a new city and to a new house. My parents think that this is a good reason to throw things out and clean up. Most things I don't use anymore. For example, I still have my first pair of school shoes, which I haven't worn for ten years!

I will try to get rid of at least 60 percent of what I have. Many toys are old and broken. But, I think a third of them will be OK to donate to a children's charity. Then there are my old books. The majority of the books are in good condition. They all hold many happy memories, and hopefully they will make other children happy, too.

1. The reason for cleaning up is for charity. ☐

2. By next Sunday, the family will have moved into their new house. ☐

3. She doesn't use the majority of toys and clothes. ☐

4. She will get rid of more than half of her childhood things. ☐

5. A lot of toys are old and broken. ☐

6. She will give 50 percent of her toys to charity. ☐

Unit 3
Food Matters

1 **Match each picture to the correct sentence.** Write the number on the line.

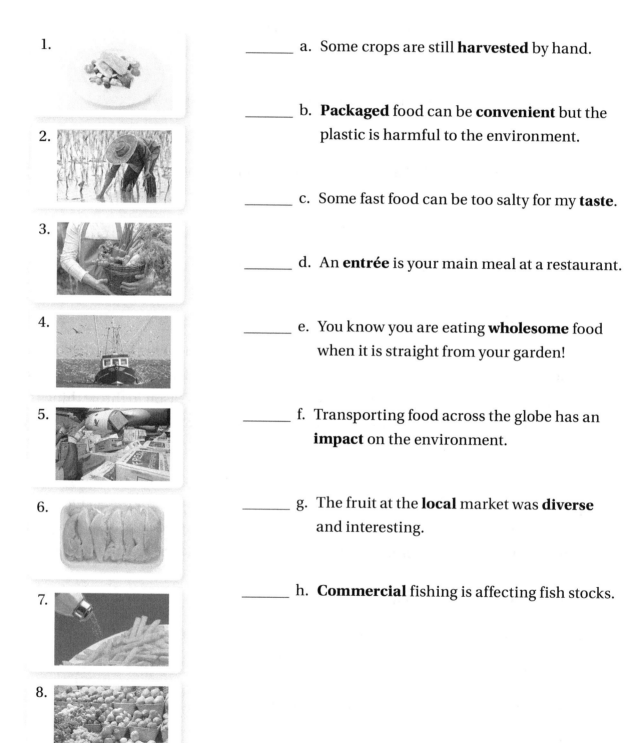

_____ a. Some crops are still **harvested** by hand.

_____ b. **Packaged** food can be **convenient** but the plastic is harmful to the environment.

_____ c. Some fast food can be too salty for my **taste**.

_____ d. An **entrée** is your main meal at a restaurant.

_____ e. You know you are eating **wholesome** food when it is straight from your garden!

_____ f. Transporting food across the globe has an **impact** on the environment.

_____ g. The fruit at the **local** market was **diverse** and interesting.

_____ h. **Commercial** fishing is affecting fish stocks.

24

2 **Fill in the blank with a word from Activity 1.**

1. French fries and fried chicken don't look very _____ to me. Let's order a chicken salad instead!

2. The tray of fresh chicken was _____ so tightly, I had to use scissors to open it.

3. The range of products they sell is very _____ . They sell clothes, toys, and food!

4. Wheat is _____ between August and September with big machines.

5. Try the _____ river trout. It's caught less than eight kilometers away, and it's delicious.

6. Farmlands in North America grow _____ crops, such as wheat, to sell globally.

7. Eating locally grown foods can have a positive _____ on the environment.

8. I love spicy food. What _____ do you have in food?

3 **Listen.** Then complete the sentences. **TR: 10**

1. His taste in food is _____ .

2. He used to help his dad _____ .

3. He buys at the local supermarket because _____ .

4. The local supermarket sells _____ .

5. One advantage of globalization is that he can _____

_____ .

6. The lamb from New Zealand is _____ .

7. Transporting foods from far away has an _____ .

8. _____ can help us make the environment better.

25

GRAMMAR

Mixed conditionals: Describing an imagined event in the past and a present result

If we **had managed** our food sources better, fewer people **would go** hungry today.
If Christopher Columbus **hadn't traveled** to the Americas, I **wouldn't be eating** potatoes right now!
If he **had added** spices, **would the fish taste** better?
If you **hadn't eaten** so much ice cream, you **might feel** better right now.

The sentence "If I had time, I would cook a healthy dinner" expresses an unreal situation in the present. Both parts of the sentence refer to the present.

The sentence "If I had had time, I would have cooked a healthy dinner" expresses an unreal or imaginary situation in the past. Both parts of the sentence refer to the past. In the mixed conditional sentences in this unit, we contrast an imagined event in the past (using the past perfect), with a present result (using *would*, *might*, or *could*).

If + past perfect, *would* (*might*, *could*) + verb (infinitive without *to*)

4 **Read.** Then circle the best explanation.

1. If they had ordered wholesome food, they would feel healthier.
   a. They didn't order wholesome food, and now they don't feel so healthy.
   b. They ordered wholesome food, and now they feel healthy.

2. If Christopher Columbus hadn't traveled to the Americas, I wouldn't be harvesting potatoes in my garden now!
   a. He traveled to the Americas, and now I am not growing potatoes.
   b. He traveled to the Americas, and now I'm growing potatoes.

3. The fish would taste better if he had added spices.
   a. He didn't add spices, and the fish doesn't taste so good.
   b. He didn't add spices, and the fish didn't taste so good.

4. They would know that food packaging is bad for the environment if they had read the article.
   a. They read the article and know that food packaging is bad for the environment.
   b. They didn't read the article and don't know that food packaging is bad for the environment.

5 **Listen.** Then complete the sentences. **TR: 11**

1. If the runner hadn't followed a _____ diet,

_____ .

2. If my friend had been more _____ ,

_____ .

3. If the cook hadn't lost the _____ ,

_____ .

4. If we hadn't had so many _____ people throughout history,

_____ .

6 **Read.** Write a mixed conditional sentence.

1. I didn't follow the recipe. The entrée is a disaster.
   If I had followed the recipe, the entrée would not be a disaster.

2. Columbus brought back new and interesting food. Our food today is more diverse.

   _____

3. I moved to India last year. My taste in food is different now.

   _____

4. The farmers didn't have a good harvest. The weather conditions were terrible.

   _____

5. Julia Child wrote a recipe book. I now cook French food all the time.

   _____

7 **Write.** What would be the present result of these situations for you?

1. If I had heard the news yesterday,

   _____ .

2. If I had reflected more on the snacks I eat,

   _____ .

3. If I hadn't ignored my parents' advice,

   _____ .

8 **Listen and read.** As you read the article, think about how it relates to the unit. TR: 12

Food from the Rooftops

Caleb Harper isn't the only person researching new ways to bring farms into cities. A new company in California has developed a system of farming that uses Growbots. Growbots are greenhouses specially designed for city rooftops. What are the benefits of Growbots? Well, one benefit is that they fit into any type of space and are lighter than traditional greenhouses. The greenhouses are also hydroponic, which means that the plants don't grow in soil but in nutrient-rich water. People who use Growbots look after the plants by using cloud technology, which can track and control conditions such as irrigation (or water levels), humidity, and plant nutrition.

Many people who live in cities are already urban farmers. They grow vegetables in community or neighborhood gardens. This traditional type of farming takes time, though. It produces fewer vegetables and is very dependent on weather conditions. In addition, studies have shown that urban farming is affected by soil conditions and air pollution. However, because the Growbot system contains its plants in the greenhouses and uses recycled water, the plants are more protected and the food is safer.

It's unlikely that rooftop agriculture will replace conventional agriculture. Growbots aren't good for root crops, such as potatoes. However, they offer an excellent alternative for growing large amounts of lettuce and tomatoes. This would free up farmlands for other crops. Using Growbots would also cut down transportation costs and the negative impact on the environment. Now these vegetables would be grown and bought locally in urban areas.

Vertical farming and Growbots are the results of creative thinking. These new methods try to manage our food resources for future generations. It could be some time before we see Growbots on rooftops in every city. But when we do, we'll know where our food is coming from!

9 **Read.** Check **T** for *True* or **F** for *False.* Rewrite any false sentences as true.

	T	F
1. The Growbot farmer needs to check on the greenhouse every day.	☐	☐
2. Technology plays a part in caring for the Growbot plants.	☐	☐
3. Urban farming is not a new idea.	☐	☐
4. Growbot vegetables aren't affected by air pollution.	☐	☐
5. One of the problems of using the Growbot system is getting soil to the rooftops.	☐	☐
6. Growbots aren't heavy and can be moved easily around a rooftop.	☐	☐
7. Using the Growbot system would be more beneficial to the environment.	☐	☐
8. We will be able to buy Growbot vegetables very soon.	☐	☐

_____

_____

_____

10 **Compare and contrast Growbot urban farming with more traditional urban farming.**

Growbot Urban Farming	Traditional Urban Farming
greenhouses on rooftops lighter and easier to use	greenhouses heavier and don't use space well

11 **Write.** Using what you learned about vertical farming and Growbots, write at least three sentences that describe why new methods of urban farming are important.

_____

_____

_____

_____

GRAMMAR

Double comparatives: Describing outcomes

The more vertical farming we do, **the more** food we will be able to produce.
The more we think about our choices, **the better** our decisions will be about the food we eat.
The less packaging we use, **the fewer** problems we cause for the environment.
The fresher the vegetables, **the healthier** they are for you.

We use **the . . . the** with two comparatives to show that one thing depends on another. The first part of the comparison expresses a condition and the second part expresses an outcome or result.

The word order in each part of the comparison is: **the** + comparative expression + subject + verb. However, the subject and verb are not necessary if they are clear from the context: *Check the expiration date on the milk you get! The fresher, the better. (The fresher it is, the better it is.)*

12 **Match the sentence parts.** Write the letter on the line.

_____ 1. The more spices you use,

_____ 2. The more chemicals we use,

_____ 3. The more recipes I read,

_____ 4. The fresher the ingredients,

a. the faster we can take action.

b. the better the food will taste.

c. the greater the threat to the environment.

d. the healthier we will all be.

e. the more I cook!

13 **Listen.** Then, write a double comparative sentence with *the . . . the.* **TR: 13**

1. Yes, *the more organic food we eat, the better it is for us* _____ .

2. Yes, _____ .

3. That's right. _____ .

4. I agree. _____ .

5. I know. _____ .

6. It's true. _____ .

14 **Read the email.** Then give advice by completing the sentences.

Hi Mom and Dad,

Well, I've just finished my first week at summer camp. At first, it was a little scary not knowing anybody, but I've made some friends, so I'm not feeling so lonely.

The food, however, is another story. I haven't been eating very much because I don't like the food. It isn't really my taste. I bought some fruit at the local store, but it doesn't seem very fresh! I want to eat well. I know it's important, but some of my friends here seem to buy a lot of snacks rather than fruit or vegetables.

Next week, we all need to cook a dish from our country or region. I'm going to cook mom's famous curry recipe, with lots of vegetables and other spices. But I'm a little nervous about making it. I'm not sure how long I need to cook it. Let me know! Also, I'm not sure if I can get all the spices and ingredients here.

I'm not very organized at the moment, and I'm finding it hard to study. The teachers are nice, though. I'm learning a lot of English!

Anyway, I'll call you over the weekend.

Bye for now,

Amaya

1. You know, the longer you are there, _the more friends you'll make_ .

2. _____ , the more you'll like it.

3. Yes, _____ , the healthier it is for you.

4. Don't be nervous about cooking with curry. _____ , the better it will taste.

5. Remember, _____ , the easier it will be to study.

31

WRITING

When you write a review, you describe and evaluate something. We usually review restaurants, hotels, books, movies, and songs to inform others. In your review, you can combine facts and opinions.

Remember to use the following phrases to show your attitude:

- actually
- honestly
- more / most importantly
- (un)fortunately

- clearly
- in my opinion
- obviously

15 Organize

1. Your task is to *write a review of your favorite restaurant.* You need to include both facts and opinions about the food, the service, and the surroundings.

   Complete the chart with facts and opinions about the different categories.

	Facts	Opinions
Food		
Service		
Surroundings		

2. Plan your writing. Your first line should immediately convince your reader to read and find out more about the restaurant. Write your opening statement here:

   _____

   _____

   Write a paragraph about each of the three areas in your chart. Support your descriptions with facts and opinions.

   Finally, you need a concluding paragraph. Remind your readers why they should visit the restaurant.

16 Write

1. Go to p. 55 in your book. Reread the model and writing prompt.

2. Write your first draft. Check for organization, content, punctuation, capitalization, and spelling.

3. Check your final draft. Share it with your teacher and classmates.

32

Now I Can . . .

talk about food sustainability.

Explain why it's good to buy food locally.

☐ Yes, I can!
☐ I think I can.
☐ I need more practice.

_____

_____

Give two reasons why vertical farming is a good idea.

_____

_____

Do you think that one day we will all be eating the same food? Why? / Why not?

_____

_____

use mixed conditionals to express how things would be different.

If I _____ (read) the review,

☐ Yes, I can!
☐ I think I can.
☐ I need more practice.

_____ .

If I _____ (eat) healthier food, _____ .

use double comparatives to describe outcomes.

The more local vegetables we buy, _____ .

☐ Yes, I can!
☐ I think I can.
☐ I need more practice.

The tastier the food, _____ .

The less I eat, the _____ .

write a review of my favorite restaurant.

Write four or five sentences using the phrases from the box.

☐ Yes, I can!
☐ I think I can.
☐ I need more practice.

| honestly | more importantly | obviously | (un)fortunately |

_____

_____

_____

_____

Choose an activity. Go to p. 92.

33

Unit 4
The Footprint of Fun

1 **Find twelve vocabulary words in the word search.** Words run in any direction. The first one is done for you.

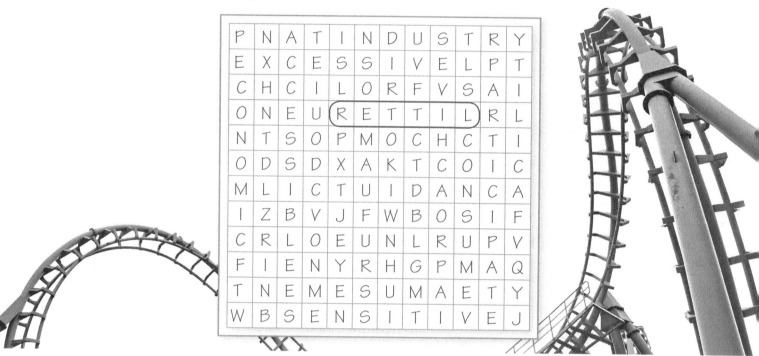

```
P N A T I N D U S T R Y
E X C E S S I V E L P T
C H C I L O R F V S A I
O N E U R E T T I L R L
N T S O P M O C H C T I
O D S D X A K T C O I C
M L I C T U I D A N C A
I Z B V J F W B O S I F
C R L O E U N L R U P V
F I E N Y R H G P M A Q
T N E M E S U M A E T Y
W B S E N S I T I V E J
```

2 **Write.** Complete the sentences with words from the word search. Make changes as needed.

1. Thousands of tons of _____litter_____ are produced at _____ parks.

2. _____ amounts of water are wasted.

3. Rides _____ a lot of energy.

4. _____ bins are important for biodegradable material.

5. Parks are _____ through two or three main gates.

6. Changes could have _____ and environmental _____.

7. All parks have bathroom _____, cafés, and shops.

8. The bright lights and noise can hurt _____ eyes and ears.

9. The entertainment _____ is trying to be greener.

34

3 **Match the sentences.** Then underline the words with the same meaning but different form.

_e_ 1. The demand for water <u>exceeded</u> the organizer's expectations.

___ 2. Some amusement parks can be an attack on the senses.

___ 3. My city has an industrial area with many factories.

___ 4. The children enjoyed going to the amusement park.

___ 5. World economies need to spend more money on clean energy.

___ 6. The famous singer is participating in a charity concert.

___ 7. There was no wheelchair access at the front gate.

___ 8. It's important to conserve areas of natural beauty.

a. His participation has been very welcome.

b. Wildlife conservation is also essential.

c. Locals want industries to improve their ecological footprint.

d. The stadium was only accessible for wheelchairs at the side of the stadium.

e. What is more, the number of bottles left on the ground was <u>excessive</u>.

f. That would have great economic and environmental benefits!

g. If you have sensitive hearing or don't like flashing lights, it can be too much!

h. They amused themselves enormously.

4 **Listen.** Number the topics in the order you hear them. Then listen again and fill in the blank with the missing vocabulary word. Finally, write a sentence about each topic.

TR: 14–15

___ a. _____ in keeping areas clean.

___ b. _____ meal

___ c. the green _____

___ d. _____ crisis

___ e. sports _____

___ f. _____ organizations

People were proactive and placed trash cans in parks.

_____

_____

_____

_____

_____

35

GRAMMAR

Passives: Describing actions and processes

We should recycle more than one in five plastic bottles.	More than one in five plastic bottles **should be recycled.**
The world population will have consumed more than 53 billion gallons of bottled water before the end of the year.	More than 53 billion gallons of water **will have been consumed** by the world's population before the end of the year.
Water companies have sold bottled water at 10,000 times the price of tap water.	Bottled water **has been sold** at 10,000 times the price of tap water.
Hopefully, other musicians will follow Jack's example.	Hopefully, Jack's example **will be followed** by other musicians.

When we use the passive voice, we focus on the action performed, not on the person performing it. The person who performs the action is not important, or is not known. We use *by* to say who did the action.

Use the passive with different verb tenses and with all modals. It always includes a form of *be* + *past participle*.

The passive is more common in formal writing and less frequent in conversation.

5 **Write.** Change the active sentences to passive. Use the correct tense.

1. The green movement has criticized the public for leaving garbage on the beach.

   People _____.

2. Starting next week, supermarkets will charge customers for plastic bags.

   Customers _____.

3. Experts are investigating the harmful chemicals in plastic bottles.

   The harmful chemicals in plastic bottles _____.

4. People have recently found a dead whale full of plastic bottles and bags.

   A dead whale _____.

5. Some bottled-water companies will have made huge profits by the end of the year.

   Huge profits _____.

6. People should use cloth bags at their local supermarket.

   Cloth bags _____.

6 **Listen.** Fill in the blank with the correct passive form of the verb in parentheses. Then listen again and complete each sentence with a suitable vocabulary word. **TR: 16**

1. An expert _____was invited_____ (invite) to talk about _____reducing_____ the school's ecological footprint.

2. _____ of the school's "green movement" _____ (see) all over the school.

3. Posters _____ (put up) to make students _____ to the important issues.

4. The posters explain what _____ _____ (cause) to the environment.

5. Paper _____ _____ (collect) by volunteers to reuse in art projects.

6. Biodegradable waste _____ (take) to _____ bins.

7. _____ _____ (collect) from the new trash cans around the playground.

8. Water fountains _____ (demand) to make water more _____ .

9. Too much water _____ (consume) from plastic bottles, which are so _____ to the environment.

10. Although at first the school board thought that more water fountains were _____ , now they _____ (install) next year.

7 **Write.** Choose a word from Group A and another from Group B. Write sentences using the passive. Use different verb tenses. Use vocabulary from the unit.

| A: | ~~wildlife~~ | rain water | tourist | electicity | facilities | amusement park |
| B: | recycle | ~~harm~~ | make | attract | build | generate |

Wildlife can be harmed by using too much plastic.

_____

_____

_____

_____

_____

8 **Listen and read.** As you read, find and underline the advantages and benefits of riding a bicycle regularly. **TR: 17**

BIKES LEAVE NO FOOTPRINTS

¹ When we think of bicycles, we think of fun and the outdoors. Bicycles give riders the freedom to explore and enjoy the environment and its surroundings. They are a healthy, cheap activity and good exercise.

² Most people know that this form of entertainment is ecologically friendly. Regular use of a bicycle has very low impact on the environment. If you are riding a bike, you are helping to reduce air and noise pollution.

³ In cities across the world, bikes are becoming more and more popular. In fact, they are becoming more than just a fun pastime. People ride bicycles to avoid traffic jams on their way to work, school, or shopping. For many people around the world, access to markets and schools would not be accessible without a bike.

⁴ Cities are taking this enthusiasm and demand for bicycles seriously. Some cities, such as Paris and Barcelona, have not only built bicycle lanes but also have introduced a system of renting bikes. You can rent, or use, a bicycle in one area of the city and drop it off at a bike station in another area of the city. Paris now has thousands of bikes for public use, with bicycle stations located throughout the city.

⁵ Some South American cities, such as Bogota in Colombia, have a weekly car-free day. More than 2 million people bicycle, skate, or jog along the 122 km (76 miles) of closed roads. On these days, the traffic-related air pollution from old buses and trucks is greatly reduced.

⁶ It seems that the bike is a force for good, providing solutions for cleaner cities without leaving a serious ecological footprint.

9 **Match each paragraph with a heading.** Write the number.

_____ a. Bicycles don't pollute.

_____ b. Bicycles also bring people together.

_____ c. Cities are being proactive.

_____ d. Bicycles are fun and good for us.

_____ e. People use bikes for work as well as for fun.

10 **List the benefits of riding a bicycle mentioned in the text.** Now think of reasons a bike might not be popular. Make your own chart and list them.

benefits of
the bike

11 **Write.** Is riding a bicycle popular where you live? Why or why not?

_____

_____

_____

_____

_____

GRAMMAR

Verbs followed by gerunds and infinitives

Verb + infinitive	Verb + gerund
She **promised to take** them to the water park.	We **enjoyed visiting** the Olympic Park.
Verb + infinitive or gerund (similar meaning)	
I **like to go** to water parks.	I **like going** to water parks.
Verb + infinitive or gerund (different meaning)	
He **remembered to go** to the park.	He **remembered going** to the park as a kid.

To remember which verbs are followed by an infinitive and which are followed by a gerund, learn them as a unit. Don't try to remember just the verb *promise*. Learn it as *promise something* or *promise (someone) to do something*. You can also use the list on p. 152 in your textbook.

Remember that some verbs, such as *forget, remember,* and *stop* can be followed by a gerund or an infinitive, but with a difference in meaning.

12 **Complete the sentences.** Use the gerund or infinitive of the verb in parentheses.

1. The swimmers invited me _____ the Olympic pool. (use)

2. The girl stopped _____ her bottle at the water fountain. (refill)

3. The fans stopped _____ to the concerts. (drive)

4. They are thinking of _____ bicycles on their next vacation. (rent)

5. Don't forget _____ the bottles in the recycling bins. (put)

13 **Listen.** Finish the sentences using an infinitive or a gerund. **TR: 18**

1. She decided _____ .

2. Next time he'll avoid _____ .

3. Don't forget _____ .

4. The local government has promised _____ .

5. Plastic waste is threatening _____ .

6. Water parks choose _____ .

14 **Read Karina's blog.** Underline the verbs and the gerunds or infinitives that follow them. Answer the questions using the verbs you underlined.

I had always <u>wanted to visit</u> the site of the 1992 Olympics in Barcelona. I like doing sports, so I will never forget visiting this Olympic venue. I loved walking in the footsteps of great athletes. It's wonderful that all the facilities have been maintained. I enjoyed seeing the views of the city from the top of the hill. When the Olympic organizers decided to build the stadium in this location, above the city, they knew what they were doing. The views are spectacular!

Barcelona planned to use all its venues after the Olympics. Although now not many locals seem to go to the stadium (you don't need to pay to visit), people go to see concerts and shows in the stadium. Next to the stadium, there's a museum that my brother wanted to see because of the interactive exhibits. However, it was a beautiful day, so he chose to swim in the pool with me. It's not every day that you can swim in a 50-meter pool where Olympic swimmers won their gold medals. I definitely suggest visiting and going for a swim. Remember to take your bathing suit!

1. What had Karina always wanted to do?

   She had always wanted to visit the site of the 1992 Barcelona Olympics.

2. What did she love doing at the Olympic Stadium?

   _____

3. What did she enjoy seeing?

   _____

4. Why did Olympic organizers "know what they were doing"?

   _____

5. What did Karina's brother want to do? What did he choose to do instead?

   _____

6. What should you remember to take with you if you visit?

   _____

7. Why do you think she will "never forget visiting" this place?

   _____

WRITING

When writing about a problem and possible solutions, we can use certain expressions.

- *Problem*: due to   it's true that   the fact is   the problem / issue is
- *Solution*: another possibility   in order to   one solution is   will result in

15 Organize

1. Your task is to *write an essay about an activity you enjoy, but that may be harmful to the environment.* You must describe why it is a problem and give three possible solutions.

   Use the chart to help you plan. Write the activity you enjoy in the first box. In the box below, make notes why the activity is harmful to the environment. Write three possible solutions, one in each of the three boxes along the bottom.

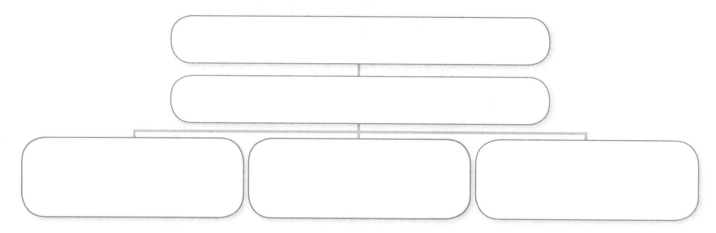

2. Plan your writing. You'll need an introductory paragraph with a topic sentence. The topic sentence, in this case, should state the activity you enjoy. Begin your second sentence with "However" and state why you think the activity is harmful to the environment. Write your topic sentence and second sentence here:

   _____

   _____

   Then, describe in more detail how this activity is harmful.

3. You will need one or two paragraphs describing your solutions for this problem. Make sure you support your ideas with facts.

   Finally, in your concluding paragraph, give your opinion on how likely it is that one of these solutions will be adopted.

16 Write

1. Go to p. 71 in your book. Reread the model and writing prompt.
2. Write your first draft. Check for organization, content, punctuation, capitalization, and spelling.
3. Check your final draft. Share it with your teacher and classmates.

Now I Can . . .

talk about the environmental impact of entertainment.

☐ Yes, I can!
☐ I think I can.
☐ I need more practice.

What form of entertainment has the greatest negative impact on the environment? Why?

_____

_____

What environmental impact has surprised you the most?

_____

_____

use passives to describe actions and processes.

☐ Yes, I can!
☐ I think I can.
☐ I need more practice.

Use passives to answer these questions.

What environmental steps are taken by Jack Johnson at his concerts?

_____

_____

What can you do personally to make a positive impact on the environment?

_____

_____

use gerunds and infinitives after verbs.

☐ Yes, I can!
☐ I think I can.
☐ I need more practice.

I enjoy _____ .

She promised _____ .

write an essay about a fun activity that may be harmful to the environment.

☐ Yes, I can!
☐ I think I can.
☐ I need more practice.

Choose an activity that you think is harmful to the environment and needs to be changed.

The issue is _____ .

One solution is _____ .

Choose an activity. Go to page 93.

43

Units 3–4 Review

1 **Read.** Complete the sentences with the correct word from the box.

commercial	consistent	diverse	entrée	harvested
impact	sustainable	vertical	wholesome	

On the 3,000 m (9,800 ft.) (1) _____ slopes of the Andes mountains, a (2) _____ variety of potatoes is grown. Some are purple, some are orange, but all are (3) _____ at this high altitude.

Potato farming here is (4) _____ with Andean culture of thousands of years ago. It's seen as a (5) _____ way of life. Recently, however, Andean farmers were pressured to grow (6) _____ varieties of potato to earn more money.

Scientists, economists, and historians are taking a proactive role and are creating seed banks to prevent these Andean potato varieties from disappearing. Top chefs from around the world are also interested in the potatoes. They are creating their next tasty (7) _____ with the unique shapes, textures, and colors of the Andean potato.

More importantly, environmentalists believe that the Andean potato, with its high levels of different vitamins, can contribute to decreasing malnutrition worldwide. Let's hope these (8) _____ potatoes can make the (9) _____ they need to survive.

2 **Read.** Use the word in capitals on the right to form a word that fits in the blank space.

Is Formula 1 racing a form of excessive (1) ___*amusement*___ ?	AMUSE
We took a closer look to find out and discovered the following. It's the actual production of the cars that harms the environment. Formula 1 racing is (2) _____ about its environmental footprint.	SENSE
Over the years, Formula 1 has shared its knowledge on reducing fuel use and on improving engines. This has (3) _____ both the environment and the car (4) _____ . It has also contributed to future car (5) _____ , the improvement of electric cars, and hybrid buses and cars.	BENEFIT INDUSTRIAL DEVELOP
Formula 1 takes its responsibility seriously and is making (6) _____ changes in many different areas. These developments bring social and (7) _____ advantages for individual car owners, too.	REVOLUTION ECONOMY
Maybe Formula 1 isn't as (8) _____ as we first thought.	HARM

3 **Listen.** Circle the correct ending to each sentence. **TR: 19**

1. The more documentaries she watches about insects and their protein,
   a. the more she wants to eat them.   b. the more documentaries she wants to watch.

2. If he had ordered a larger dish of insects, he's sure
   a. she wouldn't have the same attitude.   b. she would want more.

3. The bigger the dish of insects,
   a. the tastier they are.   b. the less tasty they appear.

4. If she hadn't traveled to so many exotic places,
   a. she would have a taste for exotic food.   b. she wouldn't have a taste for exotic food.

5. The more she reads about over-fishing,
   a. the more careful she wants to be   b. the less fish she eats.
      choosing fish to eat.

6. The better choices we make,
   a. the healthier our oceans will be.   b. the healthier we will be.

7. If she had known cacao came from the Americas,
   a. she would still be there now.   b. she would fly back every year.

8. If he had traveled as much as his friend,
   a. perhaps he would love traveling more.   b. perhaps he would like spicy food.

4 **Complete the sentences with the correct form of the verb in parentheses.** Use the passive, an infinitive, or a gerund.

1. Potatoes _____ (grow) by farmers at 3,000 m (9,800 ft.) in the Andes.

2. Scientists decided _____ (create) a seed bank for Andean potatoes.

3. We encourage people _____ (taste) the Andean potato chip.

4. My mom remembered _____ (go) to her first concert in her twenties.

5. We remembered _____ (reserve) the tickets online. It's cheaper!

6. I'm considering _____ (buy) an electric car!

7. We mustn't stop _____ (try) to reduce our plastic footprint.

8. A positive impact _____ (produce) if they work together.

9. In the future, I will avoid _____ (eat) over-fished species.

10. Car engines _____ (improve) by Formula 1 mechanics over the years.

45

Unit 5
Why We Explore

1 **Circle the word that is a different part of speech from the others.** Then use that word in a sentence.

1. | pioneer | (high-tech) | knowledge |

Explorers use many high-tech tools. _____

2. | investigate | research | curious |

_____

3. | purpose | excite | require |

_____

4. | curious | pioneer | remote |

_____

5. | achievement | investigate | expert |

_____

2 **Use a word from Activity 1 to replace each underlined word or phrase.** Make changes to the word where necessary.

1. I am <u>interested</u> to see the views from the hilltop. _____ curious _____

2. The village is too <u>far away</u>. It will take days to reach. _____

3. I want to be the <u>first person</u> who travels beyond Mars! _____

4. She is a <u>skillful</u> researcher. _____

5. His camera has very <u>sophisticated and modern</u> technology. _____

6. I want to go and <u>find out</u> what's in that cave. _____

46

3 **Listen.** Check **T** for *True* or **F** for *False*. Rewrite any false statements as true. **TR: 20**

	T	F
1. Sylvia has explored deep and remote parts of the ocean.	☐	☐
2. Research into the behavior of tropical fish has been her only achievement.	☐	☐
3. The purpose of building underwater vehicles was to allow scientists to travel easily between Pacific islands.	☐	☐
4. High-tech equipment can help stop illegal fishing.	☐	☐
5. She feels that the oceans require our immediate attention.	☐	☐

_____

_____

_____

4 **Listen again and write three of Sylvia Earle's achievements.** Then answer the question about yourself. **TR: 21**

1. _____

2. _____

3. _____

What has been your greatest achievement so far?

My greatest achievement so far: _____

_____

_____

GRAMMAR
Narrative tenses: Telling a story

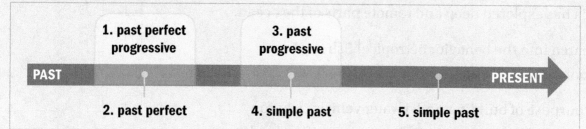

I **had been thinking** (1) of becoming a pilot for a long time. I **even had done** (2) research about flight schools. Then one day I **was talking** (3) to my cousin and he **told** (4) me I could install flight simulator software on my tablet! And that's how I **learned** (5) to fly without leaving my house!

We can use four tenses when narrating stories:
- the simple past (4, 5) for narrating events in chronological order.
- the past perfect (2) for describing an event that happened before another event in the past.
- the past perfect progressive (1) and the past progressive (3) to describe actions in progress or actions that are repeated over a longer period.

5 Read. Fill in the blanks with the correct tense for each verb. The numbers refer to the timeline shown above.

1. Lee Berger _____ (1, dig) for fossils for 17 years when he _____ (4, realize) he was looking in the wrong place.

2. In 2008, he _____ (4, go) back to South Africa and _____ (4, take) a new route to a place 17 km (10 miles) away from where he _____ (1, dig) originally.

3. As he _____ (3, walk) around, looking for clues with his nine-year-old son, he _____ (4, discover) an area with 125 new cave sites and 14 fossil caves.

4. By the end of 2009, he _____ (2, find) 700 more caves.

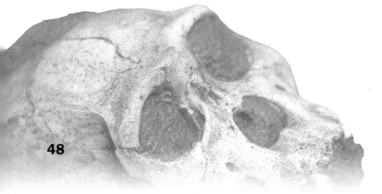

48

6 **Listen.** Fill in the blanks with a synonym from the word bank. **TR: 22**

~~drive~~	encounter		exciting
globe	remote	route	set a record

Tracey Curtis-Taylor <u>had been dreaming</u> about flying since she was a young girl. Her (1) _____ *drive* _____ for adventure started then, too. She <u>had had</u> her first (2) _____ with flying at the age of 16. When she <u>was living</u> in South Africa, and <u>had been working</u> there for many months, she <u>realized</u> that she wanted to follow her dream of flying. In 2013, she <u>flew</u> for about 16,000 km (10,000 miles) in an old airplane over (3) _____ parts of Africa by herself. In 2015, she <u>began</u> another solo flight, following the (4) _____ of pioneer Amy Johnson, who in 1930 (5) _____ for being the first female to fly solo between London and Sydney. The route <u>took</u> Tracey halfway around the (6) _____ and it was her most (7) _____ flight as a pilot so far.

7 **Fill in the chart.** Write the underlined verbs from Activity 6 in the correct columns below.

Simple Past	Past Progressive	Past Perfect	Past Perfect Progressive

8 **Write.** You and a friend had been shipwrecked on a remote island. Answer the questions to explain how you were rescued. In your answers, use at least one of the words in parentheses.

1. What had you been doing while you waited to be rescued? (investigate, look into, curious)

   _____

2. What had you done the morning of your rescue that was different from other mornings? (encourage, encountered, set a record)

   _____

3. What were you doing when you saw the rescue plane? (research, knowledge, route)

   _____

4. What did you do after the pilot landed the plane? (achievement, globe)

   _____

9 **Listen and read.** As you read, notice the reasons we should keep exploring. **TR: 23**

Will We Ever Stop Exploring?

Humphry Davy (1778–1829), a famous English chemist, was a pioneer in the field of electrochemistry. He believed that people should never stop exploring. He once said that it would be dangerous for the human mind to think that it knew everything about science and nature and that there were no new worlds to conquer.

Some people think we spend too much time and money on exploration and that we know enough about the universe we live in. But if we didn't keep exploring, we wouldn't find cures for diseases or be able to manage our ocean resources. We wouldn't have knowledge about our past or the reasons for climate change. Without exploration, we wouldn't have the technology we have today, and we wouldn't be looking into the significance of water and life on other planets and moons.

Of course, any exploration involves risks. Even as children, curiosity and the excitement of something being a little dangerous encourages us to look over a neighbor's fence or wonder what would happen if we pressed a button on a machine.

Scientists have been investigating the biological factors that make us explore. They've found that our curiosity and motivation to find and learn new things is driven by a chemical found in our brain. In some people, a high amount of this chemical can increase their level of curiosity.

Fortunately, or unfortunately, not everybody has the same amount of this chemical, which explains why we all aren't ready to zoom into space.

Whether it's curiosity, chemicals, or special genes in our DNA passed down from our ancestors—the original risk takers—there are many reasons that encourage us to keep on exploring.

10 **Read the article again.** Then circle the correct answers.

1. Humphry Davy believed that _____ .

    a. there is nothing left to explore

    b. we would be wrong to think there is nothing left to explore

2. Some people think that _____ .

    a. we know enough about the universe

    b. exploration is only about going into space

3. The chemical in our brain is _____ .

    a. only associated with children

    b. a chemical we all have

4. Curiosity and motivation _____ .

    a. encourage us to explore

    b. weren't traits our ancestors had

11 **Why do people explore?** Complete the idea web with reasons you found in the reading. Write one idea in each circle. For each reason, think of, or search the Internet for, an example from real life. Write your examples on the lines.

learn about climate change

reasons for exploring

_____

_____

_____

_____

_____

_____

_____

GRAMMAR

Geographic use of *the*

The Nile River runs through **the Sahara Desert** to **the Mediterranean Sea.**
Christopher Columbus was born in **the Republic of Genoa**, Italy. He sailed past **the Canary Islands** and across **the Atlantic Ocean** four times.
The European Union has over 500 million people.
I'm from South America. That's in **the southern hemisphere.**

We use *the* with names of mountain groups, rivers, oceans, seas, deserts, island groups, points on the globe (*the South Pole*), and general areas (*the South, the southern hemisphere*).

We don't use *the* with most countries, cities, streets, individual mountains (*Mount Everest*), islands, and continents. Exceptions are place names that contain words such as *republic, state,* or *union* (*the Dominican Republic, the United States*). We also say *the Netherlands* and *The Hague.*

12 **Write *the* or *X* for *no article*.** Then listen to the geography quiz. Circle the correct answer (**a** or **b**) to each question. Listen again and check your answers. **TR: 24–25**

1. a. _____ Himalayas   b. _____ Alps

2. a. _____ Atacama Desert   b. _____ Gobi Desert

3. a. _____ Mt. Fuji   b. _____ Mt. Kilimanjaro

4. a. _____ Britain   b. _____ United Kingdom

5. a. _____ Caribbean Sea   b. _____ Red Sea

6. a. _____ Yangtze   b. _____ Amazon

13 **Read and write.** Answer the questions.

1. What continents, seas, and/or oceans would you need to cross from your home to visit London?

_____

2. If you had a ticket to visit anywhere in the world, where would you go? Why?

_____

14 **Read the postcards.** Write *the* or *X* for *no article*. Imagine you have just visited a place you always wanted to explore. Write your own postcard. Name at least four geographical places.

Dear Kiko,

Our cruise on _____ Mediterranean Sea is going very well. It's so peaceful and calm. So far we've visited _____ Barcelona and _____ Balearic Islands. Tomorrow, we will stop at _____ Naples. We hope to see _____ Mt. Vesuvius. We've never seen a volcano in real life before! Will send you some photos.

See you soon,

Mom and Dad

Hi Mom and Dad,

How are you? Can't believe I finally made it to the top of Machu Picchu, in _____ Peru. The view over _____ Andes Mountains was spectacular! At the end of the week, we are going to travel around _____ Lake Titicaca. We will fly back from _____ Chile, but not before camping in _____ Atacama Desert and walking on the beaches of _____ Pacific Ocean. This is my dream come true! Sending love from _____ South America.

Francisco

_____

_____

_____

_____

_____

_____

_____

53

WRITING

Use the following phrases to compare and contrast how people, things, places, or ideas are similar or different.

Compare
- in the same way
- likewise
- similarly
- the same as

Contrast
- by comparison
- in contrast
- on the one hand
- on the other hand
- whereas

15 Organize

1. Your topic is to *compare and contrast exploring in the field with exploring virtually.* Look through Unit 5 in your textbook and use your own ideas about the two ways of exploring. Make notes on the Venn diagram.

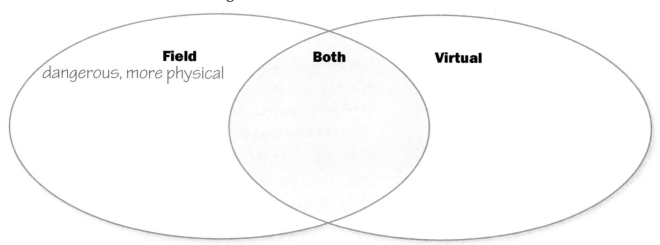

2. Plan your writing. You'll need an introductory paragraph with a topic sentence. Your topic sentence will introduce the two things you are going to compare and contrast. Write your topic sentence here:

_____

3. You'll need two to three body paragraphs. Write one paragraph describing how the two forms of exploration are similar and one paragraph describing how they are different.
4. Finally, you'll need a concluding paragraph. It will summarize your main idea and opinion on which type of exploration is best and why.

16 Write

1. Go to p. 89 in your book. Reread the model and writing prompt.

2. Write your first draft. Check for organization, content, punctuation, capitalization, and spelling.

3. Write your final draft. Share it with your teacher and classmates.

Now I Can . . .

talk about why it's important to explore.

☐ Yes, I can!
☐ I think I can.
☐ I need more practice.

How can space and ocean exploration benefit us? Write a sentence about each.

_____

_____

use narrative tenses to tell a story.

☐ Yes, I can!
☐ I think I can.
☐ I need more practice.

Describe a time (real or imaginary) when you discovered something.
Use the four narrative tenses.

_____

_____

_____

_____

use *the* correctly when talking about geographical places.

☐ Yes, I can!
☐ I think I can.
☐ I need more practice.

Write *the* or *X* for *no article.*

1. ____ Danube starts in ____ Germany and flows into ____ Black Sea.

4. ____ Russian Federation isn't part of ____ European Union.

write an essay that compares and contrasts exploring in the field and exploring virtually.

☐ Yes, I can!
☐ I think I can.
☐ I need more practice.

Would you rather work virtually or out in the field when exploring different weather conditions? Write three or four sentences and use the phrases you learned.

_____

_____

_____

_____

Choose an activity. Go to p. 94.

Unit 6
Giants

1 **Read the clues.** Unscramble the words. Then decode the sentence and decide if it is *True* or *False*.

1. nacietn — — — — —[3]— — Extremely old

2. ehportsatac — — — — — — — — —[8]— A disaster

3. dopleve — — — — — —[11]— To become more advanced over time

4. meretaid — — — — — — —[2] Distance across center of a circle

5. orensoum — — — —[9]— — Very, very big

6. tepcxenio —[4]— — — — — — — Something or someone different from others

7. tiextcn — —[1]— — — No longer exists

8. tfggnniihre — — — —[10]— — — — — Scary

9. terah — —[6]— — An organ that pumps blood

10. eghu — —[13]— — Very big

11. awj — —[5] The bones of the face where teeth grow

12. siherprotic — — — — — — — — — —[14] Time before recorded history

13. hcamots —[7]— — — — — An organ that digests food

14. geihw — —[12]— — To calculate how heavy something is

— -
[1] [2] [3] [4] [5] [6] [7] [1] [8] [3] [8] [13] [10] [3] [7] [1]

[11] [2] [3] [8] [12] [7] [1] [9] [2] [12] [14] [14] [2] [3] [6] [1] [13] [2] [3] .

True or False? _____

56

2 **Listen.** Complete the table with information about the blue whale. **TR: 26**

Length	
Type of eater	
Weight	
Heart	
Diameter of major blood vessel	
Jaw	
Stomach	

3 **Write.** Complete the information. Use vocabulary words from pp. 94–96 of your textbook.

Today, dinosaurs are alive and well in movies. They are shown as
(1) _____ creatures attacking ships in the ocean or invading
cities ready to cause a (2) _____ . They all seem to be meat-eating
(3) _____ with huge (4) _____ and
(5) _____ teeth. The film industry has
(6) _____ dinosaurs into animals with bad reputations.

However, if we look at the blue whale, huger than any dinosaur, we see an animal that
causes no harm to humans. Yet, humans have hunted blue whales very close to
(7) _____ . Fortunately, there are still between 10,000 and 25,000
blue whales in our oceans today. But are these massive mammals that seem so harmless
an (8) _____ to the rule that big is bad, or are these
(9) _____ giants just completely misunderstood?

57

GRAMMAR

Relative clauses: Defining and describing

I found a fossil **that / which** belonged to a dinosaur.	The fossil, **which** I found in my garden, was a dinosaur tooth.
Paleontologists are scientists **who** study the forms of life from prehistoric times.	Nizar Ibrahim, **who** loved dinosaurs as a boy, is now a paleontologist.
The desert **where** *Spinosaurus* bones were found was once green and tropical.	*Spinosaurus*, **whose** bones were found in the North African desert, lived on land and in water.

Some relative clauses describe or define the person, thing, or place we are talking about. We use *who* or *that* with people, *that* or *which* with things, and *where* with places.

Other relative clauses give us extra information about the person, thing, or place. This extra information is written between commas. If we leave out this information, the sentence still makes sense. *That* is not used for clauses between commas.

4 **Match the extra information from the box with each sentence.** Complete the sentences in the box with *who, which/that, where,* or *whose*.

> a. _____ many fossils have been found
>
> b. _____ eggs were the size of rugby balls
>
> c. ____ which ____ hit the Earth millions of years ago
>
> d. _____ study marine life
>
> e. _____ is downtown

1. A meteor, __c__ , caused a catastrophe.

2. In the museum, ____ , there are fossils of dinosaur teeth.

3. Scientists ____ still don't know all the secrets of our oceans.

4. Argentina and Africa, ____ , were once part of a "supercontinent" called Pangaea.

5. *Argentinosaurus*, ____ , was the largest dinosaur to live on Earth.

58

5 **Read and write.** First, complete the sentences with a word or phrase from the box. Then, combine the sentences using *that*, *which*, *where*, *who*, or *whose*.

era	fierce	preyed on	times

1. Dinosaurs left us clues. They tell us about life in a different _____ .

_____

2. Some dinosaurs were predators. They _____ other dinosaurs.

_____

3. Nizar Ibrahim is a paleontologist. He discovered the bones of a dinosaur three _____ longer than a car.

_____

6 **Listen.** Underline the clause that is not true in each sentence. Then rewrite the clauses correctly. **TR: 27**

1. *Quetzalcoatlus*, which lived 70 million years ago, was the largest bird ever.

_____

2. The Aztec god, which discovered *Quetzalcoatlus*, was a serpent with feathers.

_____

3. Scientists have found evidence that this enormous reptile had feathers on its back.

_____

4. Some scientists, whose studies focused on *Quetzalcoatlus*'s eating habits, believe it preyed on dead crabs.

_____

5. *Pterosaurs*, which was the group *Quetzalcoatlus* belonged to, were flying dinosaurs.

_____

59

7 **Listen and read.** As you read, think about what you have learned about dinosaurs. Then underline the new words you studied on pp. 100–101 of your textbook. **TR: 28**

Clues *from the Past*

Alien planets and creatures in movies such as *Avatar, Star Trek,* and *Star Wars* have always fascinated us. We have created these alien worlds in our imaginations. Yet, if these worlds did really exist, it would be very difficult to visit them. Fossils, however, allow us to travel back in time and give us a picture of a real "alien" world on our own planet. It really was an extraordinary place.

In ancient times, fossils were used for decorative or religious purposes only. However, some believed that these fossils were a sign that mythical creatures, such as dragons, existed.

Paleontology today, with the advantages of modern technology, gives us a more accurate picture of the planet before humans appeared. Animals, plants, fungi, and bacteria have all left behind significant evidence about what life was like in prehistoric times. Paleontologists can now study the tiniest details of the smallest fossils. X-ray machines, CT scanners, and advanced computer programs can analyze fossil data, reconstruct skeletons, and create the bodies and movements of extinct organisms.

But fossils tell us much more. They tell us about eating habits, which animal preyed on others, if there was enough food, and how an animal might have died. They tell us about climate. Air bubbles inside ancient trees allow scientists to study the chemistry of the oxygen inside. This can tell them if, for example, there were volcanic eruptions or other changes in the atmosphere at the time.

In paleontology, no piece of information is useless. Each piece forms a picture of our planet before we even knew it existed. Every new discovery not only creates new mysteries, but also adds a deeper understanding of how life developed.

8 **Read "Clues from the Past" again.** For each answer, write the question based on the text.

1. _____

They allow us to travel back in time.

2. _____

No, some people thought fossils were evidence of mythical creatures.

3. _____

One of the advantages is that it gives paleontologists more accurate information.

4. _____

Fossils also tell us about animal behavior and climate millions of years ago.

5. _____

No, because with each new piece of information, we understand more about how life developed.

9 **Complete the idea web to summarize what we learn from fossils.** Add ideas you have from your textbook and from this unit so far.

physical appearance of dinosaurs

Fossils

10 **Write.** When you walk in a park or in your neighborhood, what evidence do you see of the past? What can you learn about the past from what you see?

_____

_____

11 **Write.** What evidence do we as individuals leave behind?

_____

_____

61

GRAMMAR

Reduction of relative clauses

The dinosaur **(that) he found** had massive jaws.
The scientist **(who/that) I read about** had made a significant discovery.
The fossils **(which) they discovered** in the cave were well preserved.
Scientists **who study** fossils are called paleontologists. (Scientists **studying** fossils . . .)
Sequoias are gigantic trees **that are** found in California. (Sequoias are gigantic trees **found** in California.)

The relative pronoun (*that, who, which*) can be left out if there is a new subject and verb following it: *The book **(that)** I read was about dinosaurs.*

If the relative pronoun is followed directly by a verb, it cannot be left out. Sometimes we can use the verb in the *-ing* form or a past participle instead: *The scientists **who study / studying** . . .*

12 **Rewrite the statements, reducing the clauses.** Then listen and check **T** for *True* or **F** for *False*. **TR: 29**

	T	F
1. They are the largest invertebrates that live on the planet.	☐	☐
2. Scientists who study them spend a lot of time under water.	☐	☐
3. The giant squid that the researchers discovered has the biggest eyes in the animal kingdom.	☐	☐
4. Their eyes allow them to see things that other animals wouldn't see.	☐	☐
5. They have eight arms and two longer tentacles that help them swim.	☐	☐

13 **Read the letter.** Underline the relative clauses. Choose four to rewrite as reduced clauses.

Dear Mom and Dad,

Surprise! I've written you a letter, <u>which you can hold in your hands</u>, instead of just another e-mail.

The family <u>who I am staying with</u> is very friendly. This weekend, they took me to a place <u>that is called Loch Ness</u>. I learned that "loch" is a Scottish word <u>that means "lake."</u>

There are stories of a Loch Ness monster, called Nessie, <u>that go back to the sixth century</u>. The famous photo of Nessie, <u>which was taken in 1934</u>, kept the legend alive for years and years. But it was just a model of a dinosaur head <u>that floated on a toy submarine</u>. It was created, apparently, by an unhappy journalist.

There are still reports from people <u>who say they have seen the prehistoric creature</u> because they can clearly see its huge long neck. For hours we sat by the lake and enjoyed the picnic <u>that we had brought</u>. There wasn't an ancient dinosaur to be seen!

See you soon,

Tammy

WRITING

If we answer the 5 Ws: *who*, *what*, *when*, *where*, and *why* (*how* is also included in this group) when writing a news report, then we will make sure we include all the necessary details about the situation we are describing. We should try to include most of this information near the beginning of the report. That way, our reader understands what the topic is about and will want to read more.

14 Organize

1. Your topic is to *write a news report about a discovery of a giant of the past or the present.* You can use a topic from this unit or another giant that you find interesting. Think of 5 Ws and *How* that you are going to answer. Write each question on a line in the chart. Look back through the unit or do some research on the Internet to make sure you can answer your questions.

_____	_____
_____	_____
_____	_____

2. Plan your writing. You'll need an introductory paragraph with a topic sentence. Your topic sentence will state what your news report will be about. Write your topic sentence here:

_____

Try to answer your questions in the first paragraph. Use the remaining one or two paragraphs to add extra information.

Finally, you'll need a concluding paragraph. It will summarize why the discovery of the giant you have chosen is extraordinary.

15 Write

1. Go to p. 105 in your book. Reread the model and writing prompt.

2. Write your first draft. Check for organization, content, punctuation, capitalization, and spelling.

3. Write your final draft. Share it with your teacher and classmates.

Now I Can . . .

talk about giant plants and animals of the past and present.

☐ Yes, I can!
☐ I think I can.
☐ I need more practice.

Would it be possible to have giant animals like dinosaurs today?
Give your reasons.

_____

_____

Which giant do you find the most extraordinary? Why?

_____

_____

use relative clauses to define and describe.

☐ Yes, I can!
☐ I think I can.
☐ I need more practice.

Nizar Ibrahim, _____ loves his work, was determined
to find *Spinosaurus*.

The place _____ *Argentinosaurus* once lived was Patagonia in Argentina.

use reduced relative clauses.

☐ Yes, I can!
☐ I think I can.
☐ I need more practice.

Reduce the following clauses.

I watched a documentary that explained how some reptiles were able to fly.

_____

Anyone who visits a Natural History Museum will be able to travel back in time.

_____

write a news report about a discovery from the past or present.

☐ Yes, I can!
☐ I think I can.
☐ I need more practice.

Write 5W questions about a giant from this unit.

_____

_____

_____

_____

_____

Choose an activity. Go to p. 95.

65

Units 5–6 Review

1 **Read.** Write the correct word in the blank.

achievement	driven	encounter	globe	~~high-tech~~
investigate	look	motivation	pioneer	purpose
remote	route	set	traits	

Exploration New and Old

Endurance is a new (1) _____high-tech_____ underwater vehicle. Its
(2) _____ is to (3) _____ the ocean floor of the Antarctic.
This is really just a test before *Endurance* is sent to Jupiter's (4) _____ moon,
Europa. NASA is curious to (5) _____ into what lies under Europa's frozen
surface and will use *Endurance* to find out. Of course this (6) _____ is still
in the future.

Endurance actually gets its name from the ship that (7) _____ Ernest
Shackleton used to sail halfway across the (8) _____. His goal was to reach
the Antarctic and to (9) _____ a record by
being the first to cross this continent.

The expedition was (10) _____ by his
energy, enthusiasm, and (11) _____.

Unfortunately, the *Endurance* got trapped in the ice. The
crew tried to cut a (12) _____ through the ice manually but didn't succeed.

Shackleton's goal suddenly changed from polar exploration to rescuing all of his 27
men. He had all the (13) _____ of a great explorer, but saving his crew
members became his greatest (14) _____.

2 **Listen.** There are two statements for each description. Circle the best answer. **TR: 30**

1. The dinosaur described is an *carnivore / herbivore*.
   It was preyed on by *Tyrannosaurus Rex / Giganotosaurus*.

2. The ancient pyramids were discovered recently *near the Nile River / under the sea*.
   The pyramids are *huger / older* than the Egyptian pyramids.

3. The giraffe's heart is bigger than *a newborn baby's heart / a whale's heart*.
   A giraffe's heart is 61 cm (24 inches) *long / in diameter*.

4. For the speaker, the experience of climbing to the top of the world's tallest building would
   be *useless / frightening*.
   The views from the outdoor observatory *are an advantage / show ancient monuments*.

66

3 **Read.** Then circle the best answer.

The book *Around the World in Eighty Days*, (1) **which / that** was written by the French author Jules Verne, described the start of a new global tourism in the late nineteenth century.

The main character, Phineas Fogg, was a rich man (2) **which / who** had been living alone for many years. He had recently employed a Frenchman, (3) **whose / who** name was Passepartout, to be his assistant. One day, while he (4) **was reading / had read** the newspaper at his club, he saw an article about a new section of railway that (5) **opened / had opened** in India. It was now possible to travel around the world in eighty days. Phineas's friends encouraged him to take the trip. They agreed to pay him £20,000, (6) **that / which** was a lot of money in those days, if he was successful.

As they (7) **were traveling / had traveled** eastward around the globe, Phineas and his assistant had many adventures. They also discovered that the newspaper article had been wrong about the railway line. They had had to buy an elephant (8) **X / that** could take them along that route.

Thanks to the time difference, the two travelers managed to make it back across (9) **the / X** Atlantic from (10) **the / X** United States, in eighty days—in time to win the money for their achievement.

4 **Underline the relative clauses.** In your notebook, rewrite the sentences that can be reduced.

Dear Mom and Dad,

The trip is going really well. I have visited the places that you recommended.

I'm very glad that I did. My favorite place was where you both first met.

It was interesting to meet Johan, who was the best man at your wedding.

It's a shame I couldn't meet Great-Aunt Gloria who lives in Rome, but she is on vacation herself!

See you soon,

Gina

Unit 7
Creative Problem-Solving

1 **Follow the steps.** Read and cross out the words listed below. Then write a definition of the word that's left and say why it's important.

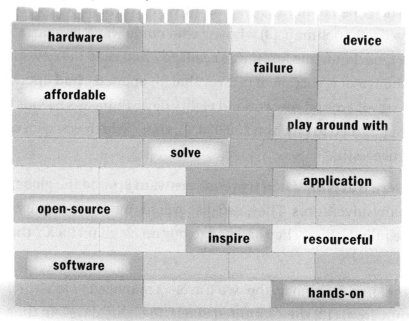

Cross out:

1. the word that describes a tool or machine made for a special purpose.
2. the word that describes the physical, electrical part of a computer.
3. the word that means to find an answer or explanation to a problem.
4. the word that means not too expensive.
5. the expression that describes what you do when you experiment with ideas.
6. the word that is associated with software that everyone can use.
7. the word that describes programs that are run on a computer.
8. the expression that describes an active way of learning by actually doing practical activities.
9. the word that means to encourage someone to do something creative.
10. the word that means you have creative ideas to deal with different situations.
11. the word that describes putting something into practical use.

The word left is _____ .

_____ is _____ .

It's important because _____

_____ .

68

2 **Listen to the interview.** Fill in the blanks with the words from the box. Listen again and circle the correct answers. **TR: 31–32**

| affordable | failure | hands-on | maker labs | software | solving |

1. The school's recent _____ have attracted
   media attention / the interest of a computer company.

2. _____ learning is encouraged by
   failure / maker labs.

3. The maker lab was _____ thanks to **parents'**
   support / funding.

4. _____ the problem of where to put the lab was **easy / not easy**.

5. The school bought hardware and _____ , but also more
   reference books / devices.

6. Students aren't afraid of _____ because it's part of
   a computer program / being an innovator.

3 **Unscramble the words.** Write the questions.
Then write your answers.

1. you / who / what / inspires / or

   _____

   _____

2. everyday / you / device / what / helps

   _____

   _____

3. are / resourceful / you / how

   _____

   _____

4. ideas / now / playing / what / around / are / with / you

   _____

   _____

69

GRAMMAR

Wish and *if only*: Expressing wishes and regrets

I wish our school had a 3D printer.

I wish 3D printers were more affordable.

I wish our school had bought open-source software.

I wish they would stop copying my designs!

If only I could inspire young children.

If only our school could have maker labs.

If only my innovation had been successful.

We use *wish/if only* + simple past to express a wish (when you want a situation to be different). Remember to use *were* for the verb *to be*.

We use *wish/if only* + past perfect to express a regret about something in the past that cannot be changed.

4 **Unscramble the words.** Write the sentences. Then listen and match each situation to the corresponding sentence. Write the number on the line. **TR: 33**

_____ a. software / had / I / the / I / wish

_____

_____ b. hands-on / were / a / if only / person / I

_____

_____ c. it / I / worked / wish

_____

_____ d. us / wish / time / she / I / more / had given

_____

_____ e. problems/ earlier / would detect/ researchers / brain / if only

_____

70

5 **Read.** Change the form of each underlined word to complete the first sentence. Then complete the second sentence with the correct tense of the verb provided in parentheses.

1. I didn't _____interpret_____ the data correctly.

   If only my <u>interpretation</u> _____ (be) correct.

2. This device will not benefit _____ people.

   I wish this device _____ (benefit) <u>people with disabilities.</u>

3. The maker lab _____ the library at my friend's school.

   If only a similar <u>transformation</u> _____ (happen) at our school!

4. The hardware didn't have a _____ connection.

   I wish the hardware _____ (be connect) <u>wirelessly</u>.

5. They didn't _____ my technical problem.

   If only they _____ (find) a <u>solution</u> to my technical problem.

6 **Write sentences about wishes or regrets.** Use *if only/I wish* and an appropriate word from the box for each situation.

affordable	approach	experiment	failure	interpret	solve

1. You are very nervous before your test.

   _____

2. Your school isn't very hands-on.

   _____

3. You want to buy new software but it's too expensive.

   _____

4. You experimented with the 3D printer and detected a problem.

   _____

5. Your headset reads brainwaves incorrectly.

   _____

71

7 Listen and read. As you read, consider some reasons that people don't always succeed at first. TR: 34

No Success without Failure

A How many times have you wondered, "Why didn't that work out?" about something you did? How many times have you thought, "If only . . ."?

B History shows us that there is no need to worry. The message from inventors and explorers, from scientists and artists, is that every cloud has a silver lining. If at first you don't succeed, try again, because there is no success without failure.

C Behind every invention we see around us, there are endless hours of playing around with ideas, of planning and persistence, and thousands of stories of rejection and failure.

D For example, take the first commercial light bulb that revolutionized the world in 1879. It took Thomas Edison 10,000 unsuccessful attempts to produce it. When a reporter asked him how it felt to fail 10,000 times, Edison simply replied, "I didn't fail 10,000 times. The light bulb was an invention with 10,000 steps!" Likewise, Oprah Winfrey, the famous talk show host, was not discouraged from appearing on television when producers told her she did not have a good TV image. Now, even though she grew up in poverty, she owns her own TV network and, she is one of the world's most successful women.

E Henry Ford designed the lightest car ever made. However, it took so long to finalize his prototype that one company lost interest and another company rejected a lot of his ideas. Ford didn't like to be hurried or have others interfere. In the end, he set up his own company, which is still successful today.

F Walt Disney's famous Mickey Mouse character was rejected at first for being too scary. Later Disney was fired from his first job and was told he had no original ideas!

G These examples, and thousands more, show us that we should never be discouraged. We should see life as a mountain of solvable problems. Each failure is a learning experience we should use to move forward and improve.

8 **Match each paragraph with a summary.** Write the letter.

_____ 1. To do something well takes time.

_____ 2. Failure can make people lose their jobs.

_____ 3. It's important to stay positive.

_A__ 4. We all experience failure.

_____ 5. We should never give up.

_____ 6. Every invention has a story to tell.

_____ 7. We have examples of failure and success from the past.

9 **Write.** From the reading, list the different ideas that express failure and success. Then add one of your own.

There is no success without failure.

_____

_____

_____

_____

10 **Imagine that a friend has difficulty with a task.** What advice would you give him/her?

_____

_____

_____

_____

_____

_____

_____

GRAMMAR

Adverbs: Expressing different levels of intensity

People's imaginations are **quite** surprising. (+)
I **sort of** hope her invention will do well. (–)
It's **rather** difficult to understand the concept. (+)
He **completely** forgot to bring his equipment. (+)
The wireless device has **hardly** been used. (–)

We use adverbs to make verbs, adjectives, or other adverbs stronger (+) or weaker (–). These adverbs are called intensifiers.

(+) *so, very, really, extremely, certainly, quite, rather*
(–) *slightly, somewhat, kind of, sort of*

The adverb *quite* can be (+) or (–) depending on the word that follows.

11 **Listen.** As you listen to the conversations, underline the intensifiers. Then circle the intensifier that has the same effect as the underlined word. **TR: 35**

1. A: Some scientists can be really shy. (**very**) / **hardly**

   B: That's true. Some are practically terrified if they have to talk in public. **almost** / **barely**

2. A: The design of this device is quite complicated. **sort of** / **extremely**

   B: You're right. I could hardly figure it out myself. **completely** / **barely**

3. A: The young inventor was somewhat disappointed. He didn't win at the science fair. **slightly** / **so**

   B: Yes, but he's very determined. He'll compete again. **sort of** / **really**

4. A: It's so exciting when young inventors realize they can change the world. **rather** / **kind of**

   B: Yeah. And the amazing thing is that some are extremely resourceful. **totally** / **sort of**

12 **Write.** In your notebook, write sentences with the words provided.

1. really / inspiring
2. kind of / wanted
3. almost / solved
4. quite / disappointing
5. hardly / a surprise
6. completely / amazing

74

13 **Read part of an interview with Jack Andraka.** Underline the adverbs of intensity. Then read the statements below and check **T** for *True* or **F** for *False*. Rewrite the false statements to make them true.

How did you get involved in cancer research?

When a very close family friend died from cancer, it made me <u>really</u> want to find a way of detecting cancer earlier. I wanted people to have a <u>much</u> better chance of surviving.

It's <u>extremely</u> sad that a lot of people die every day from the disease, and it <u>certainly</u> motivated me in my research. I also want to make sure that more people know how <u>absolutely</u> important it is to donate to research.

How do you manage school and work?

After school, I <u>almost</u> always go to the lab to work on my projects. I <u>barely</u> go out, but I do have a social life. I have learned to balance study, work, and travel.

What's your main goal in life?

My goal is to be <u>completely</u> committed to innovation and finding further solutions to problems in medicine and the environment.

	T	F
1. Jack hardly knew the friend who had died of cancer.	☐	☐
2. The death of a friend made Jack very determined to find a way to detect cancer sooner.	☐	☐
3. Donating to cancer research is almost unnecessary.	☐	☐
4. He can hardly do school work and lab work on the same day.	☐	☐
5. Jack practically never goes out.	☐	☐
6. He sort of finds it difficult to balance study, work, and travel.	☐	☐
7. He is totally committed to being an innovator.	☐	☐

_____
_____
_____
_____

WRITING

We use exemplification essays to illustrate a topic with examples. If you choose good examples, you can support your topic better as you make it more accurate, believable, and interesting. Remember to use phrases such as:

- for example
- examples include
- specifically
- to demonstrate

- for instance
- to illustrate
- such as

- a good example is
- in particular
- namely

14 Organize

1. Your task is to write an *exemplification essay about a common problem and how an everyday object could be used to solve it*. Think of a common problem and what object could help you. Research *life hacks* on the Internet to help you come up with ideas for several uses of your simple object. Write a list of the different uses of your object below.

Simple Object	
Uses	

2. Plan your writing. You'll need an introductory paragraph that will describe how you experienced a common problem. Your topic sentence will introduce the context. Write your topic sentence here:

3. You'll need two to three body paragraphs to describe other uses you discovered for the object that helped you solve your problem.

4. Finally, you'll need a concluding paragraph. Here you can give your opinion about how useful the object you used is.

15 Write

1. Go to p. 123 in your book. Reread the model text and writing prompt.

2. Write your first draft. Check for organization, content, punctuation, capitalization, and spelling.

3. Write your final draft. Share it with your teacher and classmates.

Now I Can . . .

talk about problems and how people can solve them creatively.

☐ Yes, I can!
☐ I think I can.
☐ I need more practice.

What is the role of failure in creativity?

_____

_____

What do you do when you have a problem to solve?

_____

_____

use *wish* and *if only* to express wishes and regrets.

☐ Yes, I can!
☐ I think I can.
☐ I need more practice.

Write three sentences to express your wishes and regrets about your experience with technology. Refer to the present, the past, and the future.

_____

_____

_____

use adverbs to express different levels of intensity.

☐ Yes, I can!
☐ I think I can.
☐ I need more practice.

Complete the sentences. Use your own ideas with adverbs of intensity.

Teen inventors _____ .

You have to be _____ to be an innovator.

He was _____ about using the 3D printer.

write an exemplification essay about using an everyday object to solve a common problem.

☐ Yes, I can!
☐ I think I can.
☐ I need more practice.

What problems can you solve by using baking soda?
Give some examples using the expressions you've learned.

_____

_____

_____

Choose an activity. Go to p. 96.

Unit 8
Art Connections

1 **Complete each sentence with a word from the box.** Make any necessary changes to have the word fit the sentence. Then match each sentence to the correct picture. Write the number.

| depict | perspective | preserve | primitive | reaction |

____ a. Some art is controversial and can cause a strong _____ .

____ b. The artist's style draws us in and makes us see the subject from a different _____ .

____ c. The mural _____ her love of nature.

____ d. There are many techniques to restore and help _____ paintings from damage.

____ e. We finally tracked down the cave with the _____ cave paintings.

2 **Read.** Circle the best answers.

Since prehistoric times, humans have wanted to leave their **medium /(mark)** on the world. Historians think that many of the images scratched on trees or rocks were just **symbolic / controversial**. This was probably how early humans **drew in / came up with** a way to mark their territory or identify where food and water could be found. At some point, **artwork / primitive** man thought of ways to **track down / preserve** their work better by using new **techniques / powers**. Research suggests that the earliest humans traveled quite far to **depict / track down** the minerals they needed to help them paint and make their paintings last.

It was a great **medium / accomplishment** by early humans to paint on cave walls. They used simple tools, had little light, and feared wild animals that were roaming outside their caves. It was quite a **dramatic / controversial** situation to paint in! What would our ancestors' **reaction / power** be if they could see us taking photos on our cell phones today?

3 **Listen.** Write the question for each description of a piece of art. Use one word from the box in each question. Each word can only be used once. **TR: 36**

accomplishments	come up with	draw in	~~depict~~	medium	reaction

1. What *does the painting depict?* _____

2. What _____

3. What _____

4. What _____

5. What _____

6. What _____

GRAMMAR

Reported speech: Describing what others say

"A good image should communicate instantly."	He explained that a good image should communicate instantly.
"Images are still effective, otherwise we wouldn't use them."	The photographer pointed out that images were still effective, otherwise we wouldn't use them.
"You must use an image. It's worth a thousand words!"	She told us we had to use an image because it was worth a thousand words.
"The landscapes I saw yesterday made me cry."	He claimed the landscapes he had seen the day before had made him cry.

When we report what somebody else says, we may need to change the verb tenses as follows:

Simple past / present perfect → past perfect
Past perfect / should / would → stay the same
Some modal verbs change: *must* → *had to*

We usually have to change the pronouns and adverbs of time and place. This is because you may be reporting in a different situation or context, or at a later time.

"I saw the exhibition **here last week**." – She said that **she** had seen the exhibition **there the week before**.

Remember to use different reporting verbs to add variety.

4 **Listen to the quotes about photography.** Complete the sentences using reported speech. Then underline the reporting verbs. **TR: 37**

1. He suggested that the eye _____.

2. She pointed out that photography _____.

3. She claimed that the smallest thing _____.

4. He pointed out that a photographer _____.

5. She reflected that the best photo _____.

6. He explained that his photos _____.

5 **Read.** Use the words from the box to fill in the blanks. Then complete the sentences using reported speech.

accomplishment	admiring	artwork	contemporary	critic
dramatic	impressive	preserved	reaction	themes

"You must see Michelangelo's *Creation* when you visit Rome next week, Ana," advised my friend, Paolo, who also happens to be an art (1) _____ . "I prefer (2) _____ art, modern techniques, and bold colors," I explained. "And I don't like religious (3) _____ ," I added. "It'll be an experience you'll never forget!" he insisted. So I tracked down the Sistine Chapel in the Vatican but couldn't see this famous painting. "I can't find Michelangelo!" I declared after 20 minutes. A lady nearby whispered, "You should try looking up!" I did and my (4) _____ was too loud and (5) _____ . "This is the most (6) _____ painting I've ever seen!" I exclaimed. Faces turned with a "Shhhh!" and I realized that they had all been (7) _____ the ceiling. The painting really draws the room in, and despite being over 500 years old, the colors are really well (8) _____ . It's such an (9) _____ ! How did Michelangelo depict these scenes on this high, horizontal surface? I texted Paolo, "This (10) _____ has given me a neck ache!"

1. Paolo suggested that Ana _____.

2. Ana explained that _____.

3. She added that _____.

4. He insisted that _____.

5. A lady whispered that _____.

6. Ana claimed that _____

_____.

6 **Write.** Report three memorable things family or friends said to you last week. Use different reporting verbs.

1. My sister declared that she had just finished her painting for art class. _____

2. _____

3. _____

4. _____

81

7 **Listen and read.** As you read, notice the similarities and differences between Slinkachu and Willard Wigan. TR: 38

Tiny People, BIG Places

When we think of urban art, we probably think of big bold walls with artwork on them. But it's not just big bold pieces that make an impact. Small figures can produce a big reaction, too.

Slinkachu is a British artist who creates small worlds in big urban landscapes. He uses one-centimeter high figures from train sets for his characters. The figures are plain gray when Slinkachu buys them, but he comes up with different ways to paint them. He also collects a lot of objects to use as props. These are small objects that help to build a scene. For example, a bottle top could be a boat, a dead insect could pull a cart, or a tennis ball could be a desert island.

Slinkachu thinks of each scene he wants to create as a miniature movie set. For instance, a hole in a wall could be a cave, or a puddle could be a lake. He glues the figures into a scene and uses the detail around them to help tell the story.

He then photographs his scenes and displays them in exhibitions. He often has to lie down in the street next to the figures to take the photo from his subjects' perspective.

The artist says that working in the street can be difficult because people or police stop to ask what he's doing. He also has to wait until the light or weather conditions are right so that the characters look real in their environments and don't just look like little plastic toys. His themes seem to be about the sadness of city life, and his scenes usually tell stories of fear and loneliness. He says that although we may think of places around the world as being very different, people experience the same kind of feelings.

After Slinkachu takes his photo, he leaves his little people for others to find and collect. He likes to think that their stories continue, just like those of real people we pass in the street in a moment and never see again.

8 **Read.** Then check **T** for *True* or **F** for *False*. Rewrite the false statements to make them true.

	T	F
1. Slinkachu's figures fit into the eye of a needle.	☐	☐
2. Each miniature scene tells a story.	☐	☐
3. He takes photos of his figures from their perspective.	☐	☐
4. He also takes photos of people in the street.	☐	☐
5. The right weather conditions are important for making his characters look realistic.	☐	☐
6. He uses the same figures in different settings.	☐	☐

_____

_____

_____

9 **Take notes.** Use the chart to compare Willard Wigan and Slinkachu.

	Willard Wigan	Slinkachu
Artist		
Medium		
Challenges		
Theme/Purpose		

10 **Write.** How many ideas can you think of for using a tennis ball? Be creative.

_____

_____

_____

GRAMMAR

Two- and three-word verbs

Separable

The museum **put up** *his paintings.*
The museum **put** *his paintings* **up.**
The museum **put** *them* **up.**

Inseparable

He **looked after** *his camera equipment.*
He **looked after** *it.*
She **looked up at** *the images on the ceiling.*
She **looked up at** *them.*

Some two-word verbs can be separated, but others cannot.

Many two-word verbs need an object. With **separable** verbs, the object can go either between the two parts or after: *He put **his camera** away.* OR *He put away **his camera.***

If the object is a pronoun, it must always come between the two parts: *He put **it** away.*

With **inseparable** two-word and three-word verbs, the object and object pronoun can only go after the verb parts: *He flew over **the rainforest**. He flew over **it**. He looked forward to **the exhibition**. He looked forward to **it**.*

11 **Listen.** In your notebook, write each sentence replacing the object you hear with an object pronoun. Then underline the two- and three-word verbs. **TR: 39**

1. They cleaned it off.

12 **Rewrite each sentence twice.** First, move the position of the object if it is possible. Then, replace the object with a pronoun.

1. The police tracked down the art thief.

2. They put away the equipment.

3. She went up to the famous photographer.

84

13 **Read this student's presentation and underline the two- and three-word verbs.** Then use an underlined verb phrase from the text and rewrite each sentence so that it has the same meaning.

Today I <u>looked up</u> my favorite artist, Frida Kahlo, for a presentation. I <u>found out</u> that she <u>grew up</u> in Mexico and <u>started off</u> painting in bed after a terrible accident. She was a determined woman, though. She <u>put up with</u> a lot of pain and <u>got on with</u> her life. Most of her paintings are self-portraits showing her suffering. Their bright, bold colors and painful details really <u>draw</u> viewers <u>in</u>.

She <u>fell in love</u> and married the famous Mexican artist, Diego Rivera, after she <u>asked for</u> his opinion about her artwork.

Later on in her life, Frida <u>went off to</u> Paris. People <u>raved about</u> her work and she met other famous artists, such as Pablo Picasso. Years later, back in Mexico, she had her first solo exhibition. But because she had become ill again, she <u>turned up</u> at the opening of her exhibition in an ambulance. She had to be <u>picked up</u> and carried on a bed. You have to totally admire her and her paintings!

1. The writer researched the artist. *The writer looked up the artist.*

2. The writer discovered information. _____

3. Frida spent her childhood in Mexico. _____

4. She began painting in bed. _____

5. Frida accepted a painful situation. _____

6. She continued with her life. _____

7. Her paintings attracted viewers. _____

8. Frida realized she loved Diego Rivera. _____

9. Frida wanted to know what Diego thought. _____

10. People were enthusiastic about Frida's work. _____

11. She arrived at the opening in an ambulance. _____

WRITING

When you review a piece of art, include both facts and opinions. Find out about the artist and the context in which he/she produced the art. Use this information to help you understand the art and form your own opinion about it.

Make sure you answer these questions in your review:

- What do you see?
- How did the artist create the work?
- Why did the artist create the work?

- What is your reaction to the work?
- How does it make you feel?
- What does it make you think of?

14 Organize

1. Your topic is to *write a review of a piece of artwork* that you have seen in this unit or elsewhere. Choose a piece of artwork. Do some research about the work and the artist and write the answers to the questions in the chart below.

What do you see?	How did the artist create the work?
Why did the artist create the work?	**What is your reaction to the work?**

2. Plan your writing. You'll need an introductory paragraph with a topic sentence. Your topic sentence will introduce the artwork you are going to review. Write your topic sentence here:

_____

You'll need body paragraphs with answers for each question. Remember to include facts and opinions.

Your concluding paragraph will describe your feelings and reaction to the artwork.

15 Write

1. Go to p. 139 in your book. Reread the model and writing prompt.

2. Write your first draft. Check for organization, content, punctuation, capitalization, and spelling.

3. Write your final draft. Share it with your teacher and classmates.

Now I Can . . .

talk about how art connects us across time and cultures.

☐ Yes, I can!
☐ I think I can.
☐ I need more practice.

How can we connect with a cave drawing that is over 40,000 years old?

_____

use reported speech to describe what others say.

☐ Yes, I can!
☐ I think I can.
☐ I need more practice.

Use different reporting verbs to report the following:

1. "I have been honored by the Queen."

   The sculptor _____ .

2. "You must look for Kobra's murals in Brazil next week."

   My friend _____ .

use two- and three-word verbs.

☐ Yes, I can!
☐ I think I can.
☐ I need more practice.

Choose one separable, one inseparable two-word verb, and one three-word verb.
Write two sentences with each. First, use an object, and then replace it with an object pronoun.

1. _____

2. _____

3. _____

write a review of a piece of art.

☐ Yes, I can!
☐ I think I can.
☐ I need more practice.

Answer the questions about Eduardo Kobra's mural.

1. What do you see?

   _____

2. How does the artist create his artwork?

   _____

3. Why do you think he paints?

   _____

4. What is your reaction to his work?

   _____

Choose an activity. Go to p. 96.

Units 7–8 Review

1 Read. Choose the best answer to fill in each blank.

The (1) _b_ of our lives by robotics and artificial intelligence has become a constant theme of modern times. Fifty years ago, the (2) ____ of "do-it-yourself" was popular. People seemed more (3) ____ in everyday tasks ranging from cooking and shopping to more (4) ____ jobs such as putting up shelves or fixing the car.

Now a laptop can (5) ____ what problems our car engine may have. Computers can collect information and (6) ____ it. We often talk to our (7) ____ devices, and they respond with our favorite music or with directions for the closest shopping mall.

While it's true that robots can do tasks (8) ____ well, humans will still need to (9) ____ problems creatively. For example, when there is a systems (10) ____ with our computer programs or when we need to (11) ____ whose fault it is when a driverless car crashes into another, we will probably need a human brain to analyze the problem!

What's clear is that technology will give us more free time to be (12) ____ and creative and interact with each other in more personal ways!

1. a. innovation	b. transformation	c. approach
2. a. concept	b. software	c. device
3. a. decorative	b. resourceful	c. symbolic
4. a. computer	b. affordable	c. hands-on
5. a. detect	b. turn away	c. inspire
6. a. discourage	b. solve	c. interpret
7. a. primitive	b. wireless	c. affordable
8. a. slightly	b. amazingly	c. hardly
9. a. solve	b. turn away	c. inspire
10. a. application	b. hardware	c. failure
11. a. look forward to	b. figure out	c. rave about
12. a. innovative	b. persistent	c. failures

2 Listen. Then underline the best ending for each statement. **TR: 40**

1. You can see Kobra's work *inside exhibition centers / on walls in cities.*

2. His accomplishment comes from a combination of *color and the people he paints / brushes and the spray cans he uses.*

3. Kobra's portraits *take us back in time / are copied from books in bookshops.*

4. Before Kobra paints, he *changes his clothes and behavior / researches his own themes.*

5. One of the reasons he paints is *to see if he can get away with painting on buildings / to help preserve historical buildings.*

3 **Read.** Fill in each blank with a word from the box. Make any necessary changes to the verbs.

figure out	**get off**	**look down on**	**look forward to**
point out	**rave about**	**stay**	**track down**

Last year, my parents planned a vacation on a tiny island in the Atlantic. It wasn't the Caribbean, but it still sounded great. "We're going to stay in a really nice hotel," my mom (1) _____ , and quickly added, "and you'll have Internet!" I was really (2) _____ it. I repeated, "I can't wait" throughout the day. A few weeks later, it was a different story. I wished we (3) _____ at home. As we (4) _____ the plane, there was nothing but rocks. We (5) _____ a bus and arrived at the hotel 20 minutes later. We immediately realized it wasn't the hotel in the brochure. It didn't (6) _____ a beach but on a green football field. "But people (7) _____ this place," I thought, "and the reviews were excellent!" Mom went to the front desk and tried to (8) _____ what had gone wrong. When she came back to the room, she slowly explained, "There was a storm on the other island yesterday and there is no electricity. They moved us to this island instead." "Once there is power again, we can move to the other island," my dad said. Well, at least I was able to get online so that I could talk with my friends. And we discovered a beautiful beach on the other side of the island! Maybe it wasn't so bad after all!

4 **Underline the direct speech in Activity 3.** Finish the sentences by rewriting the direct speech as reported speech.

1. Her mother pointed out that they

_____ .

2. She added that her daughter _____ .

3. The daughter repeated that _____ .

4. The daughter thought to herself how people _____

   and that the reviews _____ .

5. Her mother explained that _____

   _____ .

6. Her father commented that _____

_____ .

89

Choose an activity

Unit 1

☐ **1** Describe an extreme sport you would love or hate to do, but don't name it. Explain why you would or wouldn't like to do this sport. Use as many words from the list as you can. Ask a classmate to guess your extreme sport.

achieve	determination	enable
fashion	hazardous	mental
physical	push yourself	unbelievable

☐ **2** Read the headline. Use the sentence starters to make embedded clauses as you speculate and find out more about what happened.

Skydiver jumps from hot-air balloon without parachute!

I wonder . . .

I think . . .

I'd like to know . . .

I'm not sure . . .

Do you know if . . .

I'm telling you . . .

☐ **3** Describe a place that is special to you. Use the sentence starters to add emphasis.

The place where . . .

The thing(s) that . . .

The reason why . . .

What I like best . . .

☐ **4** **Work in pairs.** You want to do an extreme sport. Your friend tries to discourage you.

- Think of reasons for doing this sport.
- Think of reasons why your friend shouldn't do this extreme sport.
- Practice the role-play.
- Act out the role-play in class, or use a phone or tablet to make a video.

☐ **5** **Write.** Write an autobiography. Think of three main events that have helped to shape the person you are today. Describe them in chronological order.

- To plan your writing, follow the steps on p. 10 of your workbook.
- Share your writing with your teacher and classmates.

☐ **6** You saw this advertisement for an extreme sport.

Ready to push yourself to the limit? Determined to test your own mental and physical boundaries? Not afraid to take risks? Then join our team and learn to overcome the obstacles in your way!

Respond to the advertisement. Write an email. Ask for more information about location, cost, and instructors. Explain your experience with extreme sports so far.

Write approximately 150 words.

Choose an activity   Unit 2

1 You hear on the news that there has been a volcanic eruption in Ecuador. Many villages have been affected. How could a digital humanitarian help? Use the following words as you discuss ideas with a classmate.

amount of data	big picture
collaboration	coordination
measure	monitor
process	relief
scale	situation
upload	

2 Use future tenses to comment on each situation. Support your opinions with facts and reasons.

- animals—extinct
- climate change—sea level
- cancer—cure
- renewable energy—environment
- innovations—problems communities face

3 Smartphones are changing the way we do things. Use the following quantity expressions to describe how your friends use their smartphones.

- a lot of
- over half
- the majority
- a number of

4 Work in pairs. Discuss a charity with your partner.

Use these words in your discussion.

cause	fundraiser	help out
network	volunteer	

- Research a charity.
- Discuss why your school should help the charity.
- Talk about how your school will raise money for the charity.
- Practice the dialogue.
- Act out the dialogue in class, or use a phone or tablet to make a video.

5 Write. Persuade your friends and neighbors to join you in cleaning up an area in your neighborhood. Explain why they should join you. Support your statements with facts.

- To plan your writing, follow the steps on p. 20 of your workbook.
- Share your writing with your teacher and classmates.

6 You saw this advertisement.

We are looking for a team of volunteers to help the elderly with their gardening. You must be someone who loves the outdoors and nature, is in good shape, and has good people skills.

Write an email to apply to work as a volunteer. Write no more than 150 words.

Choose an activity

Unit 3

☐ **1** You want to grow your own food. Give a presentation to your classmates about why you want to do this. Invite your classmates to ask questions. Use the following words in your presentation.

diverse	globalization	harvest
impact	local	packaged
reflection	taste	wholesome

☐ **2** Describe five ways that your life would be different now if you had done things differently in the past.

For example:

If I had continued with my cello lessons, I could be playing in a youth orchestra now.

I might have traveled to Germany if I had studied German.

☐ **3** How many different ways can you replace the underlined part of the two sentences? Use comparative phrases.

a. The more I travel, <u>the more I want to see new places</u>.

Sample answer: The more I travel, *the more interested I am in visiting new places.*

b. The less fast food I eat, <u>the less packaging will be used</u>.

☐ **4** **Work in pairs.** You and your partner are going to celebrate a special occasion with your family.

- Choose the special occasion.
- One of you wants to go to a restaurant.
- One of you wants to celebrate and cook at home.
- Assign roles.
- Practice the conversation.
- Act out the conversation in class, or use a phone or tablet to make a video.

☐ **5** **Write.** Think of a movie you have seen recently and write a review of it. Give facts and your opinion on the plot, characters, and special effects. Would you recommend the movie? Why or why not?

- To plan your writing, follow the steps on p. 32 in your workbook.
- Share your writing with your teacher and classmates.

☐ **6** You see this announcement in an English-language magazine.

Hotel Reviews Wanted
Have you ever stayed in a hotel where everything went wrong?

Write a review of the hotel explaining what happened. Recommend an alternative place to stay.

The most amusing reviews will be published in our magazine.

Write your review. Write no more than 160 words.

92

Choose an activity   Unit 4

1 When was the last time you had fun at an event? What were the positives and negatives of that experience? Compare your experience with a classmate's experience in a similar situation. Use at least five words from the list.

accessible	cost	consume
enjoyable	excessive	facilities
litter	participate	venue

2 Read the call to action poster by the No-to-Plastics Movement.

We are throwing away enough plastic to circle the Earth four times! Doctors have found plastic chemicals in our bodies! We should put more pressure on businesses to stop using so much plastic. As part of our movement, you will reuse every plastic object you have. Hopefully, by 2020 we will have seen a reduction in the use of plastic!

Rewrite the poster using the passive to describe actions and processes.

3 Help this English student with gerunds and infinitives.

I want _____ (learn) to ski or snowboard.

Soon we will have to stop _____ (do) these activities.

Climate change is threatening _____ (have) an impact on snowfall.

It's important _____ (have) snow because it provides water.

I think people will continue _____ (go) to the mountains, but not for skiing.

4 **Work in pairs.** Your town wants to attract more tourists. Here are some of the ideas they are thinking about:

- A water park
- A wildlife center
- More hotels
- An annual concert

- Choose two ideas.
- With a partner, talk about why these ideas would attract tourists. Discuss the environmental impact of each idea.
- Practice the conversation.
- Act out the dialogue in class, or use a phone or tablet to make a video.

5 **Write.** You believe that the ski industry is bad for the environment. Now it's being affected by climate change. Discuss the problems and suggest two or three solutions.

- To plan your writing, follow the steps on p. 42 of your workbook.
- Share your writing with your teacher and classmates.

6 A well-known international guidebook is looking for the world's most environmentally friendly city in your country. The city that wins will have the opportunity to build a botanical garden and visitor center.

Write your recommendation of a city in your country. Write 150 words describing the city and why it should win.

93

Choose an activity   Unit 5

1 If you could explore one place in the world tomorrow, which place would it be? Give your reasons. Use at least four words from the box.

achievement	drive	encounter
engage in	exciting	globe
high-tech	investigate	knowledge

Is your place similar to or very different from a classmate's? Talk to a classmate to find out.

2 Create a graphic storyboard in your notebook about the journey of your dreams. Describe the following:

- How will you prepare for the journey?
- What specific things will you do?
- What is happening around you as you are about to leave?
- What will happen on the journey?
- What will you see/feel/do when you get there?

Use different narrative tenses and provide illustrations.

3 Look at a map of the world. Imagine that you are flying west from Perth, in the western part of Australia, to Lima in Peru, and then to Montreal in Canada. What places would you fly over? Write down the names of:

- two continents
- two oceans
- one sea
- one lake
- five capital cities
- one mountain range
- one group of islands

Think about whether you need to use *the* before the geographical names.

4 Work in pairs. Read the following statement.

The people who go on vacation every year have an explorer gene.

Do you agree or disagree? Give your reasons.

- Prepare your reasons.
- Assign roles.
- Practice your discussion.
- Act out the dialogue in class, or use a phone or tablet to make a video.

5 Write. Compare and contrast going on vacation to the same place all the time with a vacation where you explore a new place. Use a Venn diagram to help you think about the similarities and differences.

- To plan your writing, follow the steps on p. 54 in your workbook.
- Share your writing with your teacher and classmates.

6 You have received the following email from a friend.

> **To: Lara**   **Subject: My Dad**
>
> Hi Lara,
>
> My dad's going to a conference near where you live. He has some free time on the weekend and would like to explore the area. Could you tell me about some places he could visit? He loves art and is very interested in history.
>
> Is transportation easy or should he rent a car?
>
> I look forward to hearing your suggestions.
>
> Thanks for your help!
>
> Nico

Write an email back to Nico in 150 words.

Choose an activity   Unit 6

1 Imagine you travel back in time to when dinosaurs walked on Earth. With a classmate, describe what you see. Use the knowledge you have about dinosaurs and at least five words from the box.

advantage	carnivore	develop
extinction	extraordinary	frightening
gigantic	herbivore	jaw
massive	significant	weigh

2 Make relative clauses using the information below. Use *that*, *which*, *where*, and *who*.

- mammoths / big and woolly animals / lived during last ice age
- mammoths originally from northern Africa
- ice age happened over 10,000 years ago / cause of mammoths' extinction
- primitive man lived at this time / mammoths hunted by man
- mammoths died when climate changed / relatives of today's elephants

Example: *Mammoths, which were big and woolly animals, lived during the last ice age.*

3 Help your friend reduce the relative clauses in this text.

The Giant Tortoise

The largest tortoises that are found in the world are in the Seychelles and Galápagos islands.

They can live for 150 years, which is a very long time. People say that you can tell the age of a tortoise by the rings on its shell. That's not true. Only people who record the birth of the tortoise know its true age.

And here is another interesting fact. Tortoises use the landmarks that are around them to create a map in their minds of their habitat!

4 Work in pairs. Interview a paleontologist.

- Research a young paleontologist.
- Prepare five questions.
- Assign roles.
- Practice the interview.
- Act out the interview in class, or use a phone or tablet to make a video.

5 Write. Find out about a recent discovery. The discovery could be about archaeology, space, a new species, a recent epidemic, food, health, and so on.

Write a news report about the discovery. Be sure to answer the 5 *Ws* and *How*.

- To plan your writing, follow the steps on p. 64 of your workbook.
- Share your writing with your teacher and classmates.

6 You saw this announcement on your school website.

Museum Alert!

We are putting together a guide on all the museums in our area. This will then form part of a website we are building about all the museums in the country. We need reviews from students to tell us which museums they have found the most fascinating in their local area and why.

We will include some of the reviews on our new website.

—Local Education Committee

Write your review in 120–180 words.

Choose an activity

Units 7–8

☐ **1 Work in pairs.** Your new Mars probe isn't working very well. A reporter is interviewing you about what happened. Role-play the dialogue with a classmate. Use *wish* and *if only* to express your wishes and regrets. Use at least four of the words from the box.

affordable	device	failure
flexible	play around with	persistent
software	turn away	

☐ **2** Improve this description. Vary the adverbs to express different levels of intensity.

My dad is very clever. He's just developed a very cool idea that uses renewable energy. Cities around the country are very excited to apply what he has invented. It will really change our road network. It's very amazing! Everyone is very impressed. My dad is very excited too because it's the first time an idea of his has been very successful!

☐ **3 Write.** Research different ways to use empty plastic bottles. Write an exemplification essay. Use examples to describe the different uses you've discovered for the different types of bottles.

- To plan your writing, follow the steps on p. 76 in your workbook.
- Share your writing with your teacher and classmates.

☐ **4** Read the message. Respond and give advice and encouragement.

Just found out my painting wasn't chosen for the school summer exhibition. I'm going to forget about studying art! Extremely disappointed!

Write no more than 150 words.

☐ **1** Choose a piece of art. Talk to a partner about it. Then do the following:

- Write down what your partner said using reported speech. Vary your reporting verbs.
- Take turns to read aloud the conversation you had using reported speech.

Example: *You claimed that the artwork had been painted by a child.*

In your discussion, try to include as many reporting verbs as possible.

☐ **2 Work in pairs.** Each person should cut out eight equal strips of paper. Then look through Unit 8 in your book and workbook. Write down 1 two- or three-word verb on each strip. Mix the strips together and place them face down. Turn over each strip, one at a time, and see who can be the first to make a sentence using that verb. Check meanings if necessary. Keep score!

☐ **3 Write.** You're a famous artist who has just finished a masterpiece. Write a description of your artwork. Include why it's special and how you created it.

- To plan your writing, follow the steps on p. 86 in your workbook.
- Share your writing with your teacher and classmates.

☐ **4** You just saw this announcement.

We are looking for volunteers to help out at an art gallery. Positions are available from June to August. Please apply in writing and explain why you would be a good candidate.

Write to ask for details. Use 150–180 words.